Unique Solutions

Discover the *Ability* in Learning Dis*ability*

SUZANNE CRESSWELL

Occupational Therapist/Physical Therapist

Unique Learner Solutions
Copyright © 2017 by Suzanne Cresswell

All rights reserved.
Library of Congress Cataloging-In-Publication Data

Printed and produced by Printopya.

Cover Design: reddovedesign.com
Interior Design: reneeevansdesign.com

Printed in the United States
ISBN: 978-1-947165-04-5

To Margery and Glenn, Arline and Al, my mentors and heroes, each one.

And to my husband, Tom Cresswell.

TESTIMONIAL

Our son, Brian, just graduated from college. Not that long ago my husband and I weren't sure that was possible.

Brian was diagnosed with Sensory Integration Dysfunction (now called Sensory Processing disorder) at age 4, after evaluation by a major urban medical center. Our small town medical professionals were largely unfamiliar with this unique brain wiring issue in December of 1996, so it seemed like a miracle to find occupational therapists specifically trained in sensory processing therapy in our small town. It was a true blessing because at that point Brian was unable to tolerate the typical activity of a traditional preschool setting and we were at our wits' end wondering why.

Following his diagnosis, Brian received occupational therapy from Suzanne and her fellow therapists for almost two years. We are convinced their treatment and the principles we learned started us on a course of better understanding and support for Brian's unique learning needs. Since that time, Brian has surpassed our expectations socially, athletically and academically.

The day our son successfully completed a Bachelor of Science degree, we visited Suzanne's clinic to say thank you for turning Brian's life around more than 20 years ago.

We now have high expectations for his future and for countless families like ours who, through this book, will also benefit from Suzanne's expertise, insight and caring treatment of unique learners.

CONTENTS

PREFACE

I am convinced that the very factors that contribute to a unique learner's *dis*abilities are the same factors that cause his or her remarkable *abilities*. It is *because* they think differently, see the world differently and solve problems differently that they are capable of making a massive contribution to the world. The "normal" mainstream of humanity has created problems that "normal" thinking can't always solve. We need a different approach and different is what people with autism spectrum disorder*, attention deficit disorder, Asperger's* and hyperactivity do best.

Unique learners learn differently. The unique learners throughout this book provide examples of children and adults who process information differently and come up with unusual and surprising responses. It is important to remember that these individuals may have a different way of acquiring knowledge, but that doesn't suggest that they lack intelligence. In fact, their responses are sometimes better than those generated from more typical learners. These individuals can become true difference-makers in our communities. Unfortunately, this optimism is seldom the general perception.

When students cannot follow the exact model of education made available, there is a tendency for them to be viewed as a problem. Sometimes unique learners are thought to be lazy or disruptive and, generally, an annoyance. When intelligent students who have a unique style of learning recognize themselves to be the class problem, their lack of confidence creates more obstacles to their own success. It is similar to a self-fulfilling prophecy: the adult sees them as a problem, so they become a problem.

Unique learners often feel a sense of shame. Older students whom I work with tell me that they are not what they "should" be, they are not "normal." The capabilities and talents of this population tend to be marginalized. Shame can be one of the most painful experiences for unique learners and for the people who love them. Their particular skills and abilities frequently are not relevant to the requirements of traditional education leading to traditional careers.

The irony of this injustice is that these individuals could very well change the world because they have a unique perspective. These essential members of our society are capable of causing change, development, and advancement. Though many unique learners tend to live on the outer fringe, often as a castoff of society, they are truly modern heroes. Our human community depends on these brave individuals to push the margin of our thinking.

Attempting to make a child "normal" creates shame and fear-based behaviors. I know, because of spending too much time on the wrong approach before letting these children teach me what I now appreciate. I am a physical therapist* and occupational therapist* and have worked with the developmentally delayed population for three decades. This book is a reflection of what my patients and students allowed me to witness and learn. Being a unique learner is often challenging and discouraging. Throughout these pages, we will focus on how to improve the unique learner's ability to participate in a typical educational environment. It is important to understand that the purpose is not to change the unique learner or somehow make them "normal." Instead, the strategies are meant to make life a little easier for the unique learner, parent and teacher.

* See Glossary for definition

THE BUILDING BLOCKS FOR LEARNING

The building blocks for learning begin well before we are born. We begin inside a buoyant environment within the womb, not yet directly appreciating the effects of gravity. Upon birth, the gravitational pull of the earth's surface that acts on our body begins a chain of responses. Our first physical relationship with the outside world is with gravity. When this is secure and intact, the infant can better develop the nurturing bond with their parent.

As a newborn is positioned in tummy-lying, the infant feels gravity and responds to it by lifting and turning the head, ensuring ease in breathing. The feeling of gravity (processed through the vestibular system*) is integrated with the feeling of the head moving (processed through the proprioceptive system*). With the head upright, the auditory and visual system are then in an ideal orientation to process the external environment through listening and looking.

Feeling gravity and moving the head to listen and look are all early exchanges that occur between the infant and their environment. This exchange is a continuous action that develops as we mature. Sensations from the environment as well as sensations from the infant's response to the environment are fuel for the growing brain. Organizing and translating information from one sensory center to another allows perception*, intelligence, and memory to develop.

We continually test our perception by responding to the world and obtaining feedback from our actions, making further adjustments until the desired response is obtained. This feedback process occurs throughout life and progresses at each developmental stage. The human is born with an inner drive to develop and learn. Learning, in this book, implies any means of acquiring knowledge. Learning acts as a life force.

Our brain and sensory processing system* develop through repeated experiences. Each experience is impacted by our expectations, thoughts, and beliefs. We unconsciously categorize these experiences, leading to a more expedient response with each repetition. We avoid having to recreate the wheel at each stage by lumping experiences together. Our responses become automatic and fluid. When the vestibular, proprioceptive, tactile (VPT)* and other sensory systems* integrate well, we are able to perceive and respond to our world very well.

WHO SHOULD READ THIS BOOK

Unique Learner Solutions is written for parents and teachers. Perhaps your copy of this book sits on your bedside table beside all the other to-do lists and must-read stacks of papers. I hope that even the exhausted and over-burdened adult could feel drawn to open the pages and find immediate hope and relief that there are solutions to help the learning disabled child or adult in your life.

When parents find solutions, it can be life changing for the entire family. Recently I was visited by a father of a unique learner I had worked with 15 years ago. He described how well his son was doing and, just that very day, had graduated from college. He said that "Every time I drive past your office I feel close to tears because of how far my son has come since those days in OT."

This book is also written for older students and adult unique learners to give language to what they experience on an everyday basis. The "Strategies to Try" sections located at the end of chapters three through seven can become a starting point for the unique learner to brainstorm their own ideas. Adult unique learners can be helped to customize their own approach to day-to-day living. The How to Use This Book section (that follows this Preface) is helpful to read first.

* See Glossary for definition

I hope that there is something in *Unique Learner Solutions* for my colleagues, fellow occupational and physical therapists, medical providers, and school personnel. The language throughout the chapters has been carefully chosen to provide professionals with a manner of speaking in an understandable fashion to their own patients, clients, families and students. The importance of using language our patients easily understand is paramount in promoting wellness. Research indicates that when a doctor and patient hold a similar vision of the problem, their ability to collaborate and resolve symptoms increases. It becomes imperative that our language is understandable to all those involved.

THIS WORK MADE POSSIBLE BY...

Writing *Unique Learner Solutions* would not have been possible without the encouragement and support of many, many people in my life. Both of my college-aged children challenge me to think carefully and write thoughtfully. They helped me become brave enough to complete this manuscript. My husband's support and patience helped me feel strong. My writing coach, Julie Marsh, provided me with the skill of writing by attempting to mirror her concise method of making a sentence sound like music.

I was helped by friendly editors who knew my passion for this topic and were, therefore, brutally honest with their feedback. In most instances, their good advice improved the manuscript unquestionably. Additional friends, employees and patients shared their expertise in other areas. I would like to thank Shari Arribere, Colin Bennett, Garnett Callahan, Karen Cannon, Sean Cloud, Lois Cole, Phil Copitch, Heather Haddleton, Alice Hajdu, Laurie Hallum, John Kelley, Henny* Kupferstein, Barbara Anne Lamont, Reese Legerton, Joel Marsh, Tim Marsh, Janice McLeod, Anthea Milne, Debbie Milne, Lauree Montgomery, Molly Rankin, Linda Robathan, Lori Stotko, Bev Stupek, Russell Terra, Lexi Thomas,

* See Glossary for definition

Luke VanMol, Jeremiah Walsh, Wyatt Walsh, and Kirk Wayman.

The publishing process represented a steep learning curve. My manuscript would be unrealized without the formal editing and publishing assistance provided by Ryan Sprenger at Printopya Book Printing.

Finally, I would like to thank my patients, clients, school-aged students, teachers, and parents who were the true impetus behind this work. Each chapter depicts several individuals who represent a combination of children and adults with whom I have worked during my 30 years as an occupational and physical therapist. Any similarities to real patients exist only because the experiences of unique learners can be very much alike. The names and circumstances have been changed to provide the reader with a clear understanding of the unique learner in all of us.

HOW TO USE THIS BOOK

*Unique Learner Solution*s is meant as a reference guide to improve the performance of children and adults with learning challenges*. Being a unique learner can be a difficult road and this book is intended to make that journey a little easier. It is a book written for unique learners as well as those who work with and love them.

The glossary contains definitions of terminology that may be unfamiliar. When a word is followed by an asterisk (*), you will find that word in the glossary. To minimize distraction while reading, the asterisk will only follow the word the *first time* it is used in a chapter.

I do recommend reading chapter one and two (and reviewing the glossary if you like) before reading the other chapters. This is because the ideas in these first two chapters are foundational to understanding and implementing the strategies presented in the chapters that follow. However, chapters three through eight do not need to be read in order. If you are more interested in reading about the child struggling with reading, then feel free to read chapter seven after chapter two.

At the end of chapters three through seven, a "Strategies to Try" section provides the reader with specific ideas that can be implemented immediately. You may notice a similarity between the strategies in different chapters. As you will learn as you read, this is because the underlying difficulties that unique learners struggle with are similar. This means, for example, that you should feel free to try a strategy from a chapter that covers fine motor* difficulties for a unique learner who is having trouble reading.

For the most part, these strategies do not require any additional materials (other than what you likely already have on hand). However, there are products that can be used to help your unique learner improve in specific areas. Some of these products have household alternatives. For example, a resistance bar will help strengthen the wrist for improved printing. Resistance bars come in varying degrees of stiffness. A household alternative is a hand towel twisted into a tight rope. It can provide a similar benefit by modifying the exercise slightly.

You can find these products on the resource page at www. UniqueLearnerSolutions.com. The resource page also contains other helpful information. These are provided for your benefit, so I encourage you to take advantage of them.

More than anything else, I want this book to be an ongoing reference for you. I hope that you will return to these pages for guidance throughout your unique learner's journey. As a unique learner's ability to function improves, their ability to access their potential increases exponentially. I am totally convinced that unique learners hold the potential to solve the problems of this time in history. Understand as you read this book that its entire purpose is to do just this—improve the unique learner's ability to access and use their true potential.

Throughout the manuscript, I wrestled with using plural pronouns (they, their, them) with singular subjects. Though strict literary purists would say that a singular subject (your child) should always be followed with a singular pronoun (he or she, he/she, s/he), others find the mixed usage acceptable because it is such a normal part of the way people speak currently. Some sources suggested going back and forth—he in one chapter and she in another.

In the end, I chose to use plural pronouns with singular subjects for two specific reasons. First, I didn't like the idea of alternating genders between chapters because when you read about a "him" that has this challenge and your unique learner is a "her," you might not connect in the way that is most helpful. Second, because this book is specifically about the unique learner in your life, the individual child or student is referred to so many times that using "he or she" each time was cumbersome and distracting to read. I felt confident that as you read "your unique learner," "your child," or "your student," followed by they/their, your brain will automatically read "they" as *your specific child*, regardless of your child's gender.

INTRODUCTION

Picture yourself at a train station in Italy with no knowledge of the language, no understanding of the train schedule or monetary system. You must be at a specific destination at a pre-established time to meet a friend. You stand in front of the ticket station having painstakingly entered what seem like nonsense words into your smart phone to translate. Although you have the skill and ability to do this, it requires strict attention and focus because it is a novel experience. On several occasions, you had to re-enter the information because of train station distractions. The man behind the counter is clearly growing increasingly irritated with you. The echo of the Italian voice on the loud speaker, the bustle of the families gathering together and the persistence of the long lines at the information desks combine to challenge good concentration. People flow around you, jostling and speaking quickly, adding to your tension and confusion.

After what feels like a very long time, you finally decide which train you need and attempt to speak with an attendant. This involves more translation as he doesn't speak English. You hesitate, unsure if you understand correctly. You debate returning to your hotel and simply calling off the trip altogether. Stress has you feeling irritable and worried. When you finally sink into your seat, you are exhausted.

Now imagine that chaos every day of your life.

For those fluent, or even proficient, in Italian, the difficulty seems ridiculous. In the same way, many adults cannot understand why the child in their life is unable to do the simplest thing. Simple to them, that is, in the same way that boarding a train in Italy is simple for one who speaks Italian.

This is the case for many children who are unique learners.

Parents and teachers have admitted that they fail to grasp the difficulty of their child's day. Their coaxing to "try harder" and "just focus" is intended to help. The inability of the child to put the well-meaning advice into practice results in high levels of frustration for the child, the parent, and the teachers. Teachers are often focused on areas related to academics or behavior. The parents are often focused on problems with clumsiness or following directions. The child may have expressed difficulty with making friends and the three parties never realize that the underlying issues are all from the same root cause.

In my observations and treatment of hundreds of different unique learners, I have discovered some remarkable similarities between their behaviors. Nearly all of these learners have difficulty in a similar part of their brain and body system. The messages taken in through any portion of their sensory system* can become compromised. The message cannot be coherently delivered to the brain. The brain, then, responds inappropriately. Input and output don't work. The loop between input to the brain through the sensory system and output by the body in an action taken doesn't flow smoothly. This can happen when just one small developmental building block doesn't fall properly into place.

Many of the differences in how these students learn is a problem made even worse when trying to learn in the same way everyone else learns. This book will help you develop your own strategies for teaching and parenting a unique learner. This book will help you realize that it is precisely these differences in how unique learners

* See Glossary for definition

learn that can offer tremendous benefits to both the individual and to the world in which they live.

The number of children and youth ages 3–21 receiving special education services is substantial. Some estimates exceed 13 percent of all public school students. Every year that these students move forward and enter adulthood, they continue to struggle to a greater and greater degree. Low self-esteem can further reduce self-confidence. Imagine spending the first 20 years of your life, as one of my patients explained, feeling as if you are a disappointment and a failure because you can't learn in the same way as others. Imagine looking at the person seated next to you at school, as this individual had, who seems to have no trouble doing what requires huge effort for you. Feelings of inferiority are only one by-product of the difficulties experienced by unique learners.

Children and adults with learning challenges*, in this book, are referred to as unique learners. This is because for most of this population it isn't that they can't learn, but rather that they learn in a way different from typical learners. Unique learners are people you know, work with, play with, and with whom you conduct business. Maybe you have a boss, a roommate, a spouse, or a sibling who is a unique learner. Unique learners make sense of the world in their own fashion. Frequently, they gather and collect information more quickly and in a whole-picture fashion, leaving the more typical, sequential thinker far behind. They draw unique and multiple conclusions based on data that the typical thinker may infer to have only one logical outcome. Although their heightened sensitivities may sometimes seem to get in the way of learning, often these same sensitivities contribute to heightened awareness of complex solutions that benefits us all.

In my many years as an occupational and physical therapist*, I have yet to meet an individual who has not been profoundly impacted by his or her relationship with a unique learner. At a minimum, the individual's level of compassion is heightened. They begin to see the importance of viewing concerns from a variety of perspectives. Jumping to conclusions and blaming become replaced by communication and support. Poor behavior begins to appear very distinct from actions driven by hypersensitivity. When improper punishment stops, appropriate coping strategies flourish. As parents learn to see that their child is struggling because of a sensory problem and not because of an attitude problem, they learn to support their child more effectively.

This book will help you understand and interpret what is going on in the brain and body of a unique learner. I have compiled years of data shared with me by my patients and will share with you the strategies that greatly benefit all kinds of unique learners. At the very least, I hope to enlighten those of you living, working, and experiencing the unique learner's approach to life through the stories and strategies taught to me by this vital population. It is essential that the unique learner be given an opportunity to contribute fully to our busy world. We are a population of humans who believe in bizarre concepts such as: bigger is better, more and faster productivity is good, and degradation of our resources is natural.

The perspective of unique learners, with their unique sensitivities toward themselves and the world around them, can help provide answers to questions and problems that elude the more typical and mainstream mindset. Einstein once explained that you cannot solve a problem using the same paradigm from which you created it. Unique learners operate from a different paradigm and, therefore, offer us hope.

This book will open you to a new range of possibilities in interpreting the actions of unique learners and teaching them to cope, overcome, and participate in the very joyful day-to-day existence available to each one of us. By embracing unique learners and relying on their novel approach to problem solving, you will be able to help them learn as efficiently as they can. As the reader progressing through this book you will come to see that you can help your child become more organized. You can use strategies that will gradually allow your child to demonstrate productive behavior that leads to better school, job, and social success.

WHAT TO EXPECT

In chapter 1 we will delve into an explanation of what is going on in the brain of a unique learner. The vestibular*, proprioceptive* and tactile systems*, also referred to as the VPT systems*, are introduced. Dysfunction of any of these systems can definitely affect learning. This scientific approach to the inner workings of your child will cause you to exhale and exclaim, "I knew all along that my child was always very smart. My child just had a different kind of intelligence!"

In chapter 2 we will explore how you can guide and parent a unique learner, including some of the challenges parents and teachers face. We will look at parents' concerns with a fresh approach. Natural solutions will be made obvious and they will continue to reveal themselves even long after you close this book. How to understand what motivates your child's behavior and how to act and speak to your child are made clear. While all parents are vital in the lives of their children, the role of the adult in a unique learner's life is paramount. You are the basis for their success.

In chapter 3 we meet young Ranisha and Lynette, who is a more mature adult patient. Despite their age difference, they have very similar issues. In this chapter, you will learn about living with the gifts and challenges of children and adults experiencing attention deficit hyperactivity disorder (ADHD)*. As a parent or teacher, great gains can be made as you employ methods suggested in this chapter to assist unique learners. You can help them move from agitation and chaos* to a state of coherence*. The concept of self-regulation* is explored and strategies provided. The reader will fall into these pages and experience what ADHD is. They will feel what these people feel.

On her second appointment, 5-year-old Ranisha ran through the clinic like a small tornado. Her mother was unnerved, not realizing that Ranisha was providing me with valuable information regarding her self-regulation strategies. Ranisha wanted to minimize the possibility that poor behavior would happen, as it had during the previous OT* session. In the simplistic manner of a 5-year-old, Ranisha believed that if she knew everything about the clinic and its layout then she could behave properly for her therapy session. If she quickly explored the physical environment, she felt that there would be no uncertainty and, therefore, no stress.

Ranisha's actions provided valuable information about what was happening in her brain. What appeared to be bad behavior was an attempt to ensure good behavior. Ranisha's brain was gathering data about her surroundings and responding to the data as best as she could.

In this same chapter, Lynette is a mature, 35-year-old equivalent of Ranisha. Where Ranisha moved quickly, often damaging items in her path, at 35, Lynette had shifted this overt physical action to her mental landscape. Lynette was all over the place, mentally. Her mental trip and fall errors challenged her work performance. She was unable to reliably complete familiar tasks or to organize herself in terms of time management. Perhaps most aggravating, she never fully completed the spontaneous tasks her boss assigned her. Just as Ranisha randomly ran around the clinic, Lynette randomly approached her work.

In chapter 4 we discover David and several students like him who will help illustrate what to do with your child on the autism spectrum*. The theme of this chapter is participation in a classroom curriculum and a tightly structured world while dealing with autism spectrum disorder* (ASD) and its classic signs and symptoms.

Second-grader David and tenth-grader Logan both participate in a general education curriculum. Cara, in 5th grade, is enrolled in a special day class environment. Each of these three students experience times when their behaviors are coherent* and very consistent with their environment. Frequently, however, these three students' behavior is out of sync with those around them. David becomes revved up and overstimulated* when approached too directly, preferring to run away or hide underneath a table. Logan is confused by social cues and too frequently relies on negative strategies, such as task avoidance or obvious reticence to participate. Cara is described as a "wild child." She has a disorganized approach to activities with difficulty following more than one- or two-step directions. Her movements oscillate from fast and furious to complete lethargy and sleepiness.

In this chapter parents and teachers are shown how to mindfully observe students on the autism spectrum as well as other unique learners and to bring into the student's world that which promotes the most ideal brain mode for learning. The child becomes the teacher, in this case, and the parent becomes the student. The parent will learn their child's method of making sense of their own world. If you take the time to look, the child will continually teach you what they need to be successful.

Chapter 5 introduces Claire and Adam. These two unique learners have gross motor* challenges with overall poor coordination affecting their ability to learn. The important theme of this chapter is that gross motor incoordination is really a problem with the child's ability to relate to the gravitational effects of the earth's surface. At this stage in the book, the reader will have familiarized themselves with the sensory system* and the importance that the vestibular (V), proprioceptive (P) and tactile (T) sensory systems have to do with setting up a child's brain to promote learning.

Everything about learning has to do with the VPT systems. How gravity feels and how we respond underlie most human behavior. The accuracy of our vestibular and proprioceptive systems is confirmed by our sense of touch. Our VPT systems allow us to sit without falling, to successfully reach out to a toy and not overshoot the mark. Our sense of touch and our sense of vision are also involved in this success. We learn not to oversqueeze and break a toy. We also learn not to undersqueeze and drop the toy through the collective interaction of the vestibular, proprioceptive, tactile, and visual systems. If someone urges us to hurry up, this auditory sensory information further contributes to the speed and quality of grasping the toy.

In chapter 6, our unique learners Micah and Lauren also have motor incoordination problems. In this chapter, we focus on fine motor* challenges that really just look like sloppy printing. Fine motor control* is the result of a highly integrated brain and body system, which both Micah and Lauren lack. There are a huge number of developmental milestones that must be correctly put in place before we can ask children to produce highly coordinated fine motor activities. It's not as simple as "just practice more." Poor handwriting and slow or incomplete homework are usually indicative of problems in fine motor control. The best fix is through the integration of all the sensory and motor components that impact precise movement. When, "just try harder" hasn't helped, you need to read chapter 6.

Chapter 7 introduces Noah and other children and adults who have a hard time reading. This chapter explores solutions through visual–motor* exercises, while the reader is made aware of the powerful integrative functions of each aspect of the sensory

* See Glossary for definition

system. For a student to improve their reading ability, reading needs to have importance in and of itself. In other words, we need to connect the act of reading to the enjoyment of the story or to a topic that deeply interests us. When reading becomes interesting, it gains importance to the student. Their belief in their own reading ability improves and their general academic skills are made less difficult.

Methods to promote a student's enthusiasm for reading, and to foster a positive self-esteem for trying yet again where they have failed before, are illustrated in this uplifting chapter. Strategies and concepts inspired by the recent brain biology field of study known as neuroplasticity* are also reviewed in this chapter.

Chapter 8 looks at the heroes who have overcome all kinds of obstacles to make a difference in their own lives and the lives of others. These heroes are the unique learners themselves as well as those who teach and parent the unique learner. The heroes in this chapter may think that their field of influence is limited to their classroom or their home, but my observations suggest they have reached a much, much broader platform.

While we will explore several classic learning challenges (ADHD, dyslexia*, ASD), it is important to remember that the strategies and ideas contained in each of the chapters apply to unique learners of all types, not just to those we are discussing in a particular chapter. As the adult in the unique learner's life, your strategies will come from an understanding of the VPT sensory systems* and by observing your child and your students. This book is not a recipe book; it's a game changer. For some, it's a life changer.

This book is intended to help unique learners function in an optimal way.

CHAPTER ONE

IT'S ALL ABOUT THE VPT

Older children who can't tie their own shoes, younger children who can't look you in the eye, school children who can't sit still, and adults who can't stay organized enough to hold down a job are all suffering. Even though well-meaning and loving adults in their lives have tried to help by providing extra attention, support and patience, they still have problems. You know it and they know it. They're different. Their path is often a painful one. They hurt and those who try to help them are also hurting.

A mom said to me, "It hurts my feelings when the teacher tells me my son was naughty today. How is that possible? He's so young." That mom was hurting.

A teacher said to me, "I've taught elementary school for 20 years. I've never met a child with a problem like this. What am I doing wrong? He can't even trace a line. When I ask him to put the pencil at the top of the line, he doesn't know what that means." That teacher was also hurting and feeling inadequate.

Children with learning problems can be helped, but we need to understand their problem from a new perspective. Teachers and parents must watch and learn. Each student may look very different, but their problems are of similar origin. Therefore, we need to become keen observers*, almost detective-like*, in observing and interpreting what might be going on in the brain of a unique learner.

For the school-aged child, most academic models tap into certain portions of the brain and sensory systems* more than other portions. Classroom work relies on the student's ability to use the senses to look and listen much more than using the sensory system to move and feel. Learning that takes place in a typical school classroom requires a student to be sitting at a desk, looking, listening, reading, and writing. What we consider the basics (reading, writing, and arithmetic) are not basic at all. They are very complex skills taught in classrooms that require children, even those who are kindergarten age, to sit quietly and to listen. These young students are asked to take turns, but they are unfamiliar with sequencing. Many times there is a discrepancy between what is required of a kindergarten student and what they are developmentally capable of performing.

At kindergarten and first-grade levels, students need to move. Young children need to balance their body, move their limbs, and use their sense of touch in order to make sense of what they see. At the kindergarten level, sitting still at a desk and using the eyes to look forward is insufficient for the very young brain to perceive what is around them. They must move, feel, and interact with the world to really develop their intelligence.

Up to the age of 8 years old, children must move their bodies to help mature their visual system. They rely on their sense of balance, their sense of movement, and their sense of touch for their visual system to work correctly. For all of us, our sense of balance is a function of the brain and body system known as the vestibular (V) system*. Our sense of movement is made possible by the proprioceptive (P) system*, and our sense of touch is provided by the tactile (T) system*. The VPT systems* function together to make learning possible, and this relationship between the VPT and learning is the primary focus of this book. Learning how to learn is a strategy that is the basis throughout every chapter of this solution-filled book.

Renowned psychologist Jean Piaget has contributed a huge body of research about human development. His research indicates that the human brain is not designed to process abstractions or to perform complex academic work until the brain has a concrete knowledge of the body, the world, and its physical forces. In short, the VPT sensory systems need to respond to the environment in order to develop their ability to interpret the world accurately. The child's understanding of balance and gravity, their ability to move in response to their environment and to be able to interpret their world through touch must all be intact and fully functional before abstract learning can proceed.

Up until roughly 10 years of age, looking and touching tend to be the main methods for children to explore their world. Everything gets touched and felt. Children are hard to take shopping because they touch things constantly. Children at a very young developmental age are not discerning in what they are compelled to touch. Christmas ornaments, glass figurines, even unclean items on the ground are touched.

At approximately 10 years of age, the sense of hearing becomes more developed and is integrated with vision and the rest of the sensory system. This means that a child at the age of 10 can finally be asked to "look and listen." At this stage, the eyes and ears gain importance in understanding the world over the sense of touch. The more mature child will begin to use their eyes and their vision as the primary sensory system to understand the world, sometimes excessively so. When children are older you can hear their parents reminding their child to "quit staring!"

For all school-aged children, the skill of looking and listening becomes very important. Looking and listening, however, relies on the child's sense of balance, movement, and touch. Balance, movement and touch remain crucial to ensure that the rest of the child's brain operates correctly. Reduced sensory processing* of balance (V), movement (P), and touch (T) can be the basis for many learning disabilities. Disruption to the VPT creates a profound problem in awareness and understanding.

In school, we were taught about our five senses: taste, touch, smell, sight, and hearing. We actually have seven senses. The vestibular (V) sense for balance and the proprioceptive (P) sense for registering movement are typically overlooked and underestimated. Even the correct interpretation of our sense of touch with its complex tactile (T) processing abilities is often something people aren't even aware that they have!

THE VPT SENSORY SYSTEMS

Our sense of balance is managed through a portion of our sensory system called the vestibular system. The vestibular system helps us process the feeling of gravity. It is comprised of the vestibular organs and all their connections throughout the brain and body. Vestibular awareness is mainly located in the inner ear. The small canals in the inner ear help us register the effects of gravity by movement of a fluid inside the canals that stimulate tiny hair-like fibers. The vestibular system helps our body balance by communicating this vital information to the brain.

Our sense of movement is managed through a portion of our sensory system that is called the proprioceptive system. The proprioceptive system allows for our ability to detect the movement and actions of our joints through an internal sensory mechanism. This system, comprised of the proprioceptive organs

* See Glossary for definition

and their connections, is spread throughout the body and is located in the joints and in the muscles. The joints and muscles have tiny receptors that detect even very slight movement. This important information is immediately sent to the brain where it makes sure we are operating our body correctly.

Our sense of touch is also managed through a portion of our sensory system that is called the tactile system. The tactile system allows for our ability to process touch, including pressure sensitivity as well as temperature sensitivity. While we tend to think of touch being limited to our fingertips, in reality every inch of our skin makes up the tactile organ.

We develop an understanding of the world through an integration of the information coming into our brain (sensory information) together with the information leaving our brain (motor* information). This sensory and motor integration causes our body to successfully respond to what is happening around us.

Information comes into our brain through one or more of our senses. Our senses are comprised of taste, touch, smell, sight, hearing, vestibular, and proprioceptive input as well as all their complex interactions. The brain acts as a central operating station and integrates incoming data with other data and then sends outgoing information throughout the body, leading to an appropriate physical response. In OT* school, we were taught "sensory input leads to motor output." Modulating the sensory input leads to a change in motor output.

You can see your VPT in action when you visit a souvenir shop--you not only look at things, you touch them as well. This helps your brain categorize and group items together. A healthy brain involves proper integration of the entire sensory system. The seven senses comprise the entire human sensory system. The VPT systems help create an overall balanced state to the entire brain, readying the brain for learning. These sensory systems continually activate the visual and auditory pathways to make looking and listening possible. The school-aged child is frequently encouraged to pay attention by looking and listening. Their teachers often say, "Eyes and ears forward!" The teacher or adult may not realize that to do so requires integration of movement.

These important balance, movement, and touch sensory systems are intact before birth and become very active during the first moments of life and the first stages of infancy. The correct development of the VPT systems is paramount to human growth and maturation.

THE VESTIBULAR SYSTEM

Good balance is really our vestibular (V) system working for us. One of the reasons we enjoy yoga as adults is because the varied postures stimulate our sense of balance. People who participate in yoga will tell you that they experience a calming effect as well as a sense that their mind operates with more clarity. That, in a nutshell, is what the vestibular system creates: calmness, emotional security and good balance.

The vestibular system allows for the essential connection between the human body and the gravitational pull of Earth. Gravity continually operates on our body and impacts all our actions. Our growth and development are keenly connected to our ability to master Earth's gravitational pull. After all, the feeling of gravity on our body is our first profound experience when we are born.

Not being able to appropriately feel gravity can be very disturbing and disorienting. Ask anyone who has experienced vertigo, a medical condition caused when an interruption in the ability to process movement and gravity occurs within the vestibular system, which is located in the inner ear. Being dizzy all the time is not fun. These people will tell you that extreme emotional insecurity results when their understanding of gravity is subconsciously interrupted by periods of dizziness related to vertigo. Frequently, people can tolerate the dizziness but will begin to seek medical treatment when the emotional insecurity that can cause depression and an inability to thrive manifests. It is clear that we must process the feeling of gravity to feel secure.

The vestibular system interacts with all our other senses in order to orient our body in space. When the vestibular system orients us successfully, then physical balance and emotional security develop properly. Now the brain can seek higher levels of more complex stimulation. Learning functions and intellectual reasoning can develop more fully at this stage.

In addition to responding to gravity in order to balance our body, the vestibular system also directly affects our emotional control. Students who can't control their level of activity or their emotional responses may be dealing with an over- or underactive vestibular system. They may be too easily upset or too passive.

When our vestibular system correctly informs our visual system, our ability to judge distances between objects and our depth perception improve. We are able to navigate through crowded spaces, reach out and accurately pick something up, as well as judge how much space is present between smaller things such as letters, words, and numerals.

THE PROPRIOCEPTIVE SYSTEM

The proprioceptive (P) system complements the vestibular system. It allows for our ability to detect the movement and actions of our joints through internal mechanisms rather than using sight. For example, we can close our eyes and still know that our elbow is straight when it is straight and bent when it is bent. The proprioceptors that are within the elbow joint inform the brain whether the elbow is bent or straight. While the vestibular system helps us judge our position in space*, it is the proprioceptive sense that instructs our muscles how much to move in order to navigate through space successfully.

Our proprioceptive sensory system must be functioning well for our other senses to work properly. It is the proprioceptive system that tells our back and neck to stay still so that our eyes can read words, track math problems and to successfully transfer that data from a book located on our desk to our homework worksheet in front of us. It is the proprioceptive system that allows our wrist to stay still and our fingers to move independently for printing, without our even being aware that it is operating. Without the proprioceptive system accurately informing the body, our ability to learn is compromised.

THE TACTILE SYSTEM

The tactile (T) system provides the third part of our VPT systems. As we reach for a glass of water, our vestibular system is busy judging the distance between our body and the glass, and the proprioceptive system is informing our muscles how far to reach and how firmly we must grasp the glass to pick it up. The tactile sense is the gauge that tells us that our action has been successful and sends a message that the brain will embed in the memory for future reference. We are able to store this knowledge regarding speed and accuracy of picking up a drinking glass through the complex sensory-motor system*.

Our sense of touch exists even prior to our birth. Undifferentiated tissue that eventually develops into the brain and nerves is the very same tissue that develops into the skin. The skin, the brain, and all the nerves remain intimately connected with the tactile system.

* See Glossary for definition

Even older children and adults benefit from a soothing touch to ease stress-related symptoms. Patting, soothing, and placing a calming touch on the skin has a direct impact on the brain. In this manner, tactile stimulation is used to calm a child whose brain is going a million miles an hour.

Of course, in addition to contributing to a feeling of calmness, the tactile system has the important function of helping us understand what we are feeling and touching. Any lack of tactile processing in the fingertips can result in reverting back to an earlier developmental stage. As a young child, if you can't feel things with your fingertips, you're bound to try to feel them by using your lips and tongue. "Yuck! Take that out of your mouth," says the dad of a two-year-old. When you find yourself saying that to your six-year-old, you probably have a child with reduced tactile processing who may also be a unique learner.

A student who has poor tactile processing has a reduced sense of touch. They will grasp the pencil incorrectly and press down too heavily or not firmly enough. Some students have a tactile hypersensitivity* problem and cannot tolerate the feeling of the paper when their hand slides across while printing a sentence. You can see these students inappropriately holding their pencil halfway up the utensil to avoid touching the worksheet. For these tactile hypersensitive individuals, the feeling of certain clothing textures can elicit a fight or flight stress reaction*.

Tactile input can be pleasant and unpleasant. Touch can be calming and touch can be distressing. These opposing interpretations are due to how the sense of touch registers in the brain. Tactile sensations are registered in two very different areas of the brain. In one part of the brain, touch can help an individual recognize when a problem quickly needs a reaction. The problem of touching a hot stove needs a quick reaction of the hand moving away from the hot element. An unfriendly or unfamiliar touch may require a

* See Glossary for definition

quick movement of the body away from the potential danger. In these examples, touch registers in the brain region that triggers a fight or flight stress reaction to quickly provide a response.

There is another type of touch that is familiar and welcome. This sensation of touch registers in a different portion of the brain. Because the body is not reacting to the touch as threatening, the individual is better able to appreciate and discriminate the feeling of objects and surfaces. In this tactile processing part of the brain, other sensory connections that stimulate memory and incorporate intelligence allow for a more sophisticated response to touch than just fight or flight. As a small child matures, the detailed information from their skin can help them feel and manipulate toys and objects correctly. This more complex function of touch allows for the correct degree of pressure in order to use a pencil, manage buttons and fasteners, pour from a milk jug, and handle a pet kitten.

Sometimes this "wiring" gets mixed-up so that a friendly touch can be interpreted as alarming, summoning an inappropriate danger response. Oops, a confused child ends up in the principal's office for a playground mishap that they don't fully understand.

THE VPT WORKS TOGETHER

Our relationships with ourselves, with objects, and with places and people are dependent on the correct development of the VPT sensory system. The brain and the elaborate sensory processing system make constant modifications occurring on a subconscious level in order to improve our decisions and to improve our performance.

The automatic adjustments we make to swing the racket to hit a tennis ball more accurately, to ensure that the new cookie recipe turns out exactly as planned, to enable the car to navigate the turn perfectly, and to ensure our communication is being understood by another party are all adult examples of the constant subconscious modifications and the continual give and take occurring through the VPT systems.

For school-aged children, the concepts of reading, writing, and arithmetic are dependent on the give and take of information relayed throughout the brain and body and through constant modifications in VPT sensory processing. Although it occurs on a subconscious level, unique learners must be taught to understand this invisible process. By making the VPT process more conscious, children can better participate in their own development of intelligence.

We talk about making "good choices," but what we really mean is to actively participate in the give and take that modulates*, accommodates, and improves our actions and decisions. We can improve our actions based on the current incoming sensory information as well as past experience and the memory of our past performance outcomes. This intuitive process allows us to better inform our future actions. The tennis ball goes where we planned it, the cookies turn out perfectly, and we maneuver the car correctly because of this sensory intelligence.

When any of the elements of the sensory system are compromised, function of the overall sensory-motor system is impaired. This is obvious when considering a child with an overt sensory challenge, such as deficiency in their sense of hearing or impairment in their sense of sight. Unfortunately, it is much harder to see in vestibular, proprioceptive, and tactile sensory problems. Individuals with these difficulties don't appear to have such clear deficiencies as those with hearing or visual deficits. However, the negative impact of improperly functioning VPT systems cannot be overemphasized.

THE VPT AND THE LEARNING CONNECTION

Correct operation of the VPT processing systems allow us to notice the space that exists between objects and the space between letters on a page. We learn to read as we begin to recognize the very tiny differences between the shape of one letter and another. Have you ever noticed how closely a "b" looks to a "d"? The VPT sensory system helps to discern this visual detail by allowing the brain and the body to process objects that move and objects that hold still, and to process the space between these two objects. Unless these developmental milestones are acquired naturally, future deficits can occur.

Children have a developmental need to learn. Children, and especially children who are unique learners, need to learn how to use their brain more effectively. Learning to organize their brain will help a child's brain work better. Children learn best when accessing as many sensory systems as possible. When students sit at a desk to listen or to read, they do so at the expense of important aspects of the brain being marginalized.

The problem of reduced VPT functioning can result in enormous dysfunction for any child or adult. A child may look clumsy or hyperactive. A student may have difficulty reading, organizing their backpack, or may appear lazy. The adult unique learner may be disorganized, unable to pay bills on time, hold down a steady job or enjoy long-term relationships. Children and adults with minimal brain dysfunction, learning challenges*, ASD*, sensory integration disorders*, ADHD* and people recovering from a head injury or stroke, all demonstrate reduced VPT processing. All of these individuals can be helped by strategies in this book, *Unique Learner Solutions*.

Parents and teachers need to emphasize the importance of incorporating multisensory learning*. It needs to be understood that many activities that may look like the child is merely playing

* See Glossary for definition

actually work facets of the brain that lead to adeptness in brain capacity. Sometimes you can tell by the child's level of interest (their smiles and laughter) how perfectly matched the activity is to the child's ability to learn. From this perspective, you can see the brain learning how to learn. I frequently refer to this phenomenon as "brain working here*" behavior and depict it throughout this book.

In the chapters that follow, a multitude of unique learners are introduced along with some of the strategies used to help them. When applied at home and at school, you can help your child to do better and to feel better, too. The importance of parents and teachers, whose job it is to apply these VPT strategies, cannot be expressed too strongly.

When you have a unique learner in your life, it is easy to feel overwhelmed not only by the responsibility but also by the ongoing struggle that you and your unique learner experience. Often, parents and teachers can clearly see that there is a problem, but they just don't know what to do about it. While this chapter familiarizes you with the concepts of the VPT sensory systems, chapter 2 speaks directly to parents and teachers to offer both encouragement and guidance.

CHAPTER TWO

PARENTING AND TEACHING A UNIQUE LEARNER

Let's face it: your child thinks differently. Throughout this book, you will meet a number of individuals, like your child, who think differently. Their stories illustrate the symphony of problems that can derail an individual's ability to learn. The parent or teacher of a unique learner is frequently put in a position to be the primary role model for these unique minds and, therefore, hold a very responsible role. As you read through this book, you will gain new knowledge, strategies, and methods to help your child. You will also quickly recognize and celebrate the great parenting and teaching methods that you already use.

While all children are unique and have individual strengths and weaknesses, there is a range of "typical" behavior that falls within the average stages of a child's development. If a child falls outside of this range, their life can be very challenging and genuinely exhausting. Not infrequently, the child acts differently than other children of their same age. It is important to focus on the motivating factors behind the behaviors of your unique learner even though it is tempting to convince yourself that the child is just not trying hard enough or that they are merely attempting to gain attention.

For the parent of a unique learner, there can be a great deal of stress, pain, and exhaustion. Parents must face the reality that something is "not right" with their child. While few parents hesitate to hustle their child to the doctor when they are ill, accepting that their child has a learning issue of any sort is extremely difficult. For this reason, they often urge their struggling child to try harder or to settle down and to be more careful. Their desire is for their child to fit in and excel in everyday life. Taking the first step to look beyond the behavior and ask "why questions" is the beginning of the process.

Consider the unique learner Billy, together with his friends enjoying a backyard game of tag. Children are running every which way. Billy is a child who has problems with his balance and, as a result, he runs with his arms out in front in an unconscious attempt to compensate for his poor balance. In the excitement, and when charging forward, the child's arms come in direct contact with another child. Pushed over, the child lands on the ground and complains loudly of the infraction. Billy remains bewildered and is hurt by the accusation of his friends having observed the event. Billy had no intention of pushing and, for practical purposes, no understanding of the event at all. Frequently, unique learners like Billy make errors when they attempt to join in the fun activity of others. They don't have a strategy in place to do it correctly or to change gears and to try again.

In almost every playground altercation there is an adult choice available between either a powerful learning opportunity or a timeout for poor behavior. While the adult won't always have the best circumstances and patience to opt for the learning opportunity, understanding of the child's actions provides the best opportunities to help improve behavior in the long term. It's a hard thing to understand, but Billy playing tag with his arms and hands forward was not malicious; it was a compensation for poor balance. Knowing this is the first step in truly helping Billy.

When you can, take the time to review a confusing activity together. The results will have far-reaching effects down the line to teach children like Billy how to compensate for their lack of brain and body sensory integration*. Billy can learn strategies to compensate for a dysfunctional VPT*.

A child like Billy needs to think of their actions and to think of the perspective of others when playing with friends in the backyard. Just like "when it rains, you get wet," Billy can be told, "When you run fast, your arms lift up to protect yourself and the others can get hurt." Perhaps you can point out the irony of trying to protect yourself with outstretched arms and how this can end up harming others.

Instead, a timeout with adult scolding could prevent Billy from learning through natural consequences. Of course, to the adult an abrupt timeout may seem like the safest choice for all concerned. Sometimes safety trumps all else. However, yelling and scolding that could lead to Billy's accompanying feelings of shame may inhibit his ability to remember and to learn from the event. When yelled at, Billy may only recall that something about tag got him into grave trouble. When asked what he learned, he would state, "I shouldn't play tag, I think."

UNIQUE SOLUTIONS FOR THE UNIQUE LEARNER

The unique learner's problems and their solutions are different from those of the more typically developing child. For the unique learner with their sensory problems, we want to make conscious that which is usually only in the background. When the child has better awareness, they can cope with a greater number and greater range of circumstances. The child gradually develops a sense of ease when they are taught the nuts and bolts of how to learn. Once they learn how, they can learn lots and lots and lots of things!

You can teach older children how to compensate for their lack of fine motor* precision by making these invisible and subtle sensory-motor activations more obvious. Rather than saying, "You're holding the pencil wrong," try describing exactly what you observe. You are making the invisible sensory-motor processing system visible through your description. Maybe they can't feel the hand posture very well, but when you describe it so that the child can augment the feeling of the pencil in the hand with its visual appearance, they can self-correct. Most importantly, you are teaching them a life-long strategy. You are teaching them how to learn, how to acquire knowledge.

The child who seems to lack coordination may lack the correct feedback regarding movement data entering their brain. In this case, the child needs that vital feedback through other channels. When you use words, you are appealing to their intellect. The intellect, the individual's cognitive abilities, can be an alternate way into the brain. Sometimes, that's all they really need. Rather than introducing a solution, they just need some clarification of the problem.

The step-by-step verbal information helps augment the child's VPT systems* that should really be doing this job naturally but aren't. Your child can develop strategies to fill in for the deficiencies in their VPT systems. When you make visible, through your nonjudgmental words, what seems invisible to your child, you can see the miraculous capabilities and brilliance of your unique learner. You, the adult, get to be a part of your child truly becoming a more competent individual.

I heard a young teacher say to her student, "Look at how tightly you're squeezing the pencil. Your finger muscles look like they're working very hard. Can you make your muscles work more softly?

* See Glossary for definition

Try to hold the pencil more gently." Instantly the child tried a softer grip with better printing results.

The next time your child is unsuccessful, provide them with concrete directions for success. Consider these examples: The correct way to enter Grandma's house without sliding over her shiny floors and rearranging all her rugs, the correct way to handle a new book without tearing the paper, and the correct way to eat without overstuffing the mouth can all be helped by articulating what is observed: "I see you putting lots and lots and lots of food in your mouth every single bite." Then offer a plausible and respectful nonjudgmental explanation such as, "Maybe your brain doesn't know that your mouth is already full." When possible, provide an alternative behavior: "Your tummy is going to be much happier if you take one bite and then chew and swallow before you take the next bite."

"Stop eating so fast!" is unclear and confusing for the child. Does it mean that the child is chewing too quickly? Does it mean that the child is moving their arms and hands too quickly? Does it mean that the child is wiggling in the chair too much? Similarly, the word "No!" is equally confusing. Does "No!" mean "Stop!" or does it mean "Drop what's in your hand!", "Be quiet!" or "Go to your room!"? These simple declaratives are not simple at all for a child who is lacking in their sensory processing* abilities. If you decide that "No!" means "Stop!" are you sure you want your child to stop in the middle of the street if you say the word "no"? If you decide that "No!" means "Drop that!", ensure that you do not say the word "no" when your child is holding an ice cream cone and making an unreasonable request that must be declined. The behavior you are trying to elicit by saying "No!" can be helpful in one circumstance and disastrous in another.

THE UNIQUE LEARNER AND SOCIAL INTERACTIONS

Often unique learners have trouble with social relationships due to misunderstanding the communication around them. Sometimes they are so aware of the nonverbal cues exchanged during a conversation that they have difficulty responding properly. Talking back and forth can be hard unless the topic of conversation is presented with compatible body language. The appropriate posture, facial expression, and tone of voice must match and be relevant to the words spoken. Humor, irony and satire may be very misinterpreted.

Most of us are able to interpret the meaning of words and the tone of the conversation. However, we feel perplexed when the speaker shows disinterest or impatience through their body language. Looking away, looking at a clock, or displaying tightly crossed arms can all impact a conversation. For unique learners, the speaker's nonverbal communication speaks far louder than any words.

Sadly, most of us have become accustomed to the partial attention of others while speaking. We are used to talking to someone's profile and not directly at their face or looking at their eyes. We are hurried and assume that we understand the context and meaning of the person's statement even without eye contact and compatible body language.

The cost of frequent errors, misunderstandings, and reduced work performance can be directly linked to inaccuracies in communication. How many times in one day do you feel you are misunderstood or that you misunderstood another's message to you?

These inappropriately quick exchanges that can occur in a classroom, when teachers must be focused on a large number of students, often result in confusion for the unique learner. The teacher who says, "Good job, Johnny," while also distracted by another student and not realizing that he's not actually looking at Johnny, can cause the unique learner to misunderstand the message.

The unique learner can easily become distracted by the volume or tone of the speaker's voice and the appearance of inconsistent facial or body posturing. In this case, Johnny may think to himself, "It's too stressful and confusing to hand in my paper to the teacher. I'll find a way to do it later." Meanwhile, finding a way to do it later gets forgotten. The teacher thought he was encouraging Johnny by the comment "Good job." Johnny's parents, meanwhile, are concerned about their son's inconsistent grades. They say to each other, "All he needed to do was hand in his completed assignment to Mr. Smith. Johnny had it in his backpack, I know he did!"

Students and adult unique learners like Johnny have a hard time explaining their actions. "I don't know" is sometimes a truthful answer. With deficiencies in VPT sensory processing, they are unaware of the underlying cause of their behavior. Unique learners tend to operate from a different level of sensitivity than their peers. Strange sensitivities, such as the quality of the room lighting, the sound of the traffic, and the feeling of their own clothing against their skin, often impact their performance. These confusing sensations have been present all their lives.

It is normal for many unique learners to startle every time a school bell sounds. It is a regular occurrence for many unique learners to focus so fully on overcoming their profound fear of having their hair cut, attending a dental appointment, a movie or other enjoyable event, that they are incapable of doing anything but focusing on overcoming their fear. It feels like an everyday occurrence, they don't know anything different and it can affect every aspect of the unique learners' life.

Katie was looking forward to seeing a movie with her parents. When the movie began, however, she stared straight forward, took deep breaths, and chewed on the top button of her floral shirt. The more she thought about it, she couldn't wait to leave. Time dragged on. Until the movie came to an end, Katie employed her stress management strategies so completely that there was no energy or enthusiasm available for other activities, such as light conversation, eating popcorn, or focusing on the story. Katie was short-tempered in the car on the way home and certainly did not want to stop for a milkshake! "No one understands me!" she shrieked.

Unique learners like Katie often believe that other people experience the same sensitivities. As these other individuals are able to function at school despite the sound of a school bell, deal easily with haircuts and dental appointments, and enjoy movies, they believe that everyone else is clearly coping much better. The unique learner doesn't realize that the manner in which they experience the world is different from how others experience the world. Because they believe everyone's experience is the same as theirs, the unique learner concludes that they are far inferior to their peers. Self-esteem issues can then further cloud learning and performance.

THE ROLE OF THE DETECTIVE/OBSERVER

Children who are unique learners believe there is something wrong with them. Well-meaning teachers and adults confirm this belief with admonishments to "try harder." Self-esteem can plummet as the individual becomes aware that they are unable to meet the expectation of the adults in their lives or match the achievements of their peers. Nobody realizes that there is an actual disconnect in the sensory-motor system* that may be causing the problems the child is experiencing.

* See Glossary for definition

The more lost these children become in the swamp of "normal," the more they desperately try to blend in. Acting as the class clown and other behaviors can mask and remove the attention from the real problem. Being able to see past the mask and address the underlying sensory disconnect is the work of great parents, teachers, and therapists.

Being able to see past the mask involves great detective work*. Being a detective implies nonjudgmental observation so that you can discern the difference between a unique learner's coping strategy and run-of-the-mill misbehaving. Being a detective requires a paradigm shift on the part of the adult. An occupational therapist* has specific training and experience in this type of detective work. Occupational therapists spot and treat disconnects in the sensory-motor system of their patients in schools, businesses, homes, hospitals and in the OT* clinic.

Teachers are faced with a myriad of students and their varying needs, atypical behaviors, and performance problems. Unique learners can easily be viewed as an additional irritant that no one has sufficient staff to properly cope with in the classroom. Without training, too much effort is spent on trying to get the student to act like everybody else.

Instead, teachers must learn to see these differences as clues to the student's sensory processing struggles. Parents and teachers can experience a paradigm shift while practicing the strategies and ideas suggested at the end of chapters three through seven. But first, to become a detective and nonjudgmental observer* of a unique learner presupposes three important facts:

One: A unique learner is already equipped with their own essential neurophysiologic* complement to be successful in adapting to the world around them. Through this understanding, it becomes the job of the adult observer to reserve judgment and to learn how to facilitate the child in blossoming in a harmonious and natural way.

Two: An innate drive exists in all of us reading this book for desirable organized social behavior. Psychologists refer to this behavior as "being in a zone," "following the game plan," or "in the flow." It occurs when a person is involved in a task that has meaning. Involvement in such a task provides purpose for the individual and leads to happiness and self-satisfaction. This means that if a unique learner could achieve desirable, organized social behaviors, they certainly would do so on their own. Most of the time, they are already trying to the best of their ability.

Three: Patterns can be identified that contribute to a unique learner's ability to be organized and coherent* in their actions or to be disorganized, incoherent, and chaotic* in their performance. The adult in the child's life can observe these patterns and softly shape the environment to favor that which produces the most coherent behavior in the child.

Through acceptance of the above three statements, parents and teachers can learn how to bring into the child's world that which promotes the most ideal brain mode for learning. The child becomes the teacher and the adult becomes the student. The adult's role involves learning the child's method of making sense of their own world. Through this lens, you will see that almost everything the child does has purpose. If you take the time to look, the child will continually teach you what they need to be successful.

Children can be excessively revved up and excitable or they can be excessively tuned out. When they are tuned out, they seem lethargic. Their slowed-down mood and energy level, as well as their reduced attention span, may require the assistance of a compassionate adult to help rev up their alertness. The excessively revved up child also requires the involvement of a supportive adult to calm them down. Assistance may be required initially, but ideally they learn how to move from chaos to coherence on their own.

* See Glossary for definition

CALMING THE CHAOS

The concept of being too dialed up or too dialed down, too revved up or too slowed down, thumbs up or thumbs down are all ways of characterizing an individual's level of alertness. They are metaphors. When it comes to unique learners, chaotic and erratic behavior is not a one-time thing. A strategy to handle chaos must be in place.

It's usually helpful to choose a metaphor for chaos and a metaphor for coherence that have meaning to your child. With the use of fun and familiar language, unique learners must become aware of themselves and aware of their level of alertness. They must learn how to move from one state, or one mood, to another. Eventually, they can be helped to see how their level of alertness affects their behavior and the behavior of others.

These children need to understand that acting one way in one circumstance may not be appropriate in another circumstance. A fast-moving, laughing, and screaming child at Grandma's house may not be as acceptable as a fast-moving, laughing, and screaming child on a safe children's playground. Children who are lacking VPT sensory processing abilities must develop an understanding of these nuances. They need to know when to do what.

Unique learners can be taught compensatory strategies. What their VPT sensory system* doesn't automatically feel can be experienced through other channels to the brain. Appealing to a child's intellect and discussing their behaviors helps to fill in the gaps for many sensory deficiencies. It is imperative to understand that the unique learner's incorrect actions often relate to improper VPT functioning and not just poor behavior.

Interacting with unique learners may require a change in emphasis. Full eye contact, a quiet environment, clear physical demonstrations in addition to the provision of good verbal directions may all become necessary for effective communication.

* See Glossary for definition

We must keep in mind that unique learners tend to process information differently than the rest of us. It becomes our role to support the unique learner. We need to respect their alternative capacities for gaining knowledge.

THE DIFFERENCE ONE PARENT OR TEACHER CAN MAKE

How and why you were selected to parent and educate a child with such potential to change the face of humanity is an incomprehensible responsibility. Through the approach outlined in chapters three through seven, exponential improvements in relationships with all people can be noted. Seeing unique learners through their eyes will help you gain perspective. For all of us, an intelligent exploration into the mind of a unique learner leaves a powerful imprint on our ability to be compassionate and understanding, and to strive for equality.

If just a few parents and teachers grasp the importance of these concepts, many lives will be changed as a result. If 10,000 adults are empowered to allow their children to become who they really are and use their unique brains to full capacity, the world could be changed.

The combination of the ideas in chapter one and chapter two are intended to create a fresh lens from which to view your unique learner. Keep these concepts in mind as you progress through the next five chapters. Regardless of the difficulty each unique learner has, they can improve their ability to learn and function. As you read, realize the difference a knowledgeable parent or teacher can make in the course of a unique learner's life. In chapter three, you will see that a lack of knowledge in a young learner's life can lead to life-long challenges.

Thank you for all you do, parents and teachers!

FROM CHAOS TO COHERENCE: THE ADHD PREDICAMENT

The first time I saw Ranisha, she ran through the hall and threw open the door to the children's therapy room. She began to pick up toys and throw them down, black curls bouncing as she moved swiftly from object to object. Her mother moved behind her like a late arriving vacuum, scolding and scooping up items to return them to their regular place. Ranisha's chaotic behavior was helping me evaluate exactly what her problem was. Her mother, however, was mortified and looked near tears.

As an occupational therapist*, I evaluate these busy individuals using a "detective mode*," a term I coined indicating a way of looking without judgment in order to observe unique learners. With Ranisha, my immediate goal was to better understand this unique learner's behavior and what was motivating her actions. Once I could better appreciate what the missing developmental building blocks might be, I could begin a meaningful approach to help Ranisha and her mother.

With three decades of working with this population as an occupational and physical therapist*, I have become aware that many of my patients' needs result in similar strategies to develop those missing building blocks. Even when their presenting deficits appear very different, the strategies focus on one main area. The strategies are frequently aimed to facilitate the VPT systems*. By working to develop these missing pieces, unique learners can and do move from chaos* to coherence* and are able to live much fuller and less frustrating lives.

When a unique learner is younger, the process seems less complicated. Not only are the child's negative coping mechanisms less ingrained, but the support people involved are usually very aware and highly motivated to assist. The efforts of those supportive friends and family members are, unfortunately, often too focused on correcting "bad behavior." Parents and teachers try to make the unique learner "normal." But what is needed is a celebration of the gifts of the unique learner. When parents and teachers use strategies to improve the child's already existing healthy and coherent* behaviors, the unique learner can make tremendous progress without the child being pressured to become someone that they just aren't.

As the unique learner gets older, the people around them become gradually less tolerant. What seemed like childish and inappropriate behavior for a five-year-old becomes ridiculous when seen in a teen and completely unacceptable in an adult. The efforts to help the unique learner tend to diminish over time and resentment can grow. Adult unique learners find that their co-workers and friends have little tolerance for any behavior that puts an added strain into their lives. To look and act normal, the unique learner must develop strategies for fitting into the box that culture says is "normal." But a healthier paradigm seeks strategies that allow the unique learner to accomplish the cultural norms without sacrificing their own uniqueness.

Sooner or later everyone develops strategies to deal with their strengths and weaknesses. These strategies can be productive or non-productive. Many times, unique learners need help developing the skill of recognizing the difference between a productive and a non-productive strategy and between good and bad habits.

Lynette was a 35-year-old adult unique learner who was using storytelling and blaming as her primary strategies. These strategies were designed to remove responsibility from her and place it anywhere else. Storytelling was her special kind of excuse-making and blaming was something she did constantly. Reportedly, her employer was getting tired of tolerating these worn-out and non-productive strategies.

Lynette came into our clinic for OT* intervention with a prescription from her doctor that stated, "Diminished organizational skills with difficulty sustaining full-time employment." Lynette knew that she had difficulty maintaining long-term relationships, including employment, but didn't connect that fact with any lack on her part. In her mind, all she needed was someone to help with her "weird sense of touch" and hypersensitivity to sounds. Because of these hypersensitivities, she had to keep leaving work to go home and change her clothes when she had a sudden intolerance to the touch of the clothing material or an "unbearable hum" of the overhead lights. In Lynette's mind, leaving work to change her clothes wasn't her fault. Rather, it was the weird sensitivity that was to blame. When she came to see me, she was in danger of losing her current job, and it wouldn't be the first job Lynette had lost because of what she termed "unfair employers."

Despite this disconnect, Lynette was a pleasant and kind woman with a ready smile. She had a long history of work-performance challenges, including poor timeliness, lack of organization, and the inability to keep up with the necessary documentation protocols. Lynette admitted to having difficulty attending to her alarm clock in the morning, frequently arriving to work late. She had trouble sticking to standard timeframes for completing work tasks. This behavior was becoming a huge problem for her colleagues and team members who required all work tasks to be completed consistently. They complained to the supervisor.

Lynette's emotional response to these challenges varied from a sense of being hurt, sabotaged, and victimized to a complete lack of concern. Lynette explained that she couldn't understand what "the big deal" was. In referring to timeframes, she believed that she was always capable of completing the work, just not within the standard start and stop time imposed by her supervisor. She felt misunderstood by her past employers. Lynette's support network of friends and family members reinforced Lynette's belief that she was repeatedly victimized.

Unfortunately for Lynette, it would have been much more helpful if her friends could have helped her to identify the chaos she was creating in her life. Well-meaning friends tend to have one of two responses. The first is the protective mode that Lynette's support network took. They don't want the loved one to feel bad and tend to see the good in the person; therefore, the fault must lie somewhere else, anywhere else. They make excuses for the person.

Though certainly this seems to be a kinder approach from the second method, which takes the form of reminding, nagging and badgering, neither of these approaches help the unique learner move from chaos to coherence.

There is a third approach that is helpful: using the detective mode to function as non-judgmental observer*. The observer watches and learns before judging and criticizing. Unfortunately, those who are closest to the unique learner are often in denial, fear, exhaustion or are too frustrated to do this more complex third approach. This was the case for Lynette. She needed professional help moving from chaos to coherence.

* See Glossary for definition

Lynette wanted to become calmer and steadier in her actions. She was optimistic about OT succeeding. While she was in high school, Lynette's mother had taken her to see a family friend who was an occupational therapist. Lynette recalled that her mother's friend seemed to actually understand her problems. Though she only saw the therapist for a few sessions, it was the first time that she had experienced any hope that she wasn't just a bad kid. By the time she came to see me, Lynette had already lost her second job in a six-month period and was desperate to hold onto her current position at the dental office.

Back in Lynette's high school days, her mother's friend and occupational therapist felt Lynette had a condition called attention deficit hyperactivity disorder (ADHD)*. There was little known about ADHD at that time. Most diagnoses involved hyperactivity in boys. The students who suffered from the condition were viewed as "too hyper," too lazy, or having poor motivation and bad behavior. In present times, most people are aware that attention deficit disorder involves problems with an inappropriately brief attention span and poor concentration. However, this disorder was not well known when Lynette was a child in the eighties. She recalled her school years as very problematic.

Individuals who live with ADHD deal with chaos on an everyday basis. As young students, they seem to get into trouble. Organized and productive behavior is difficult at best and can range all the way to nearly impossible. The child with ADHD needs to learn how to bring the chaos into a state of coherence so that they can live a more productive and enjoyable life. Lynette, an adult, grew up thinking that she was a bad girl. I was hopeful that I could instill a more positive self-esteem in my childhood patient, Ranisha.

Ranisha was still too young to realize that she was behaving differently from those around her. She hadn't yet learned negative coping strategies that Lynette used, such as excuse-making and storytelling. Ranisha was still trying to figure out how to live in her skin.

It isn't unusual for those who have deficits like Ranisha's to be unaware that what they deal with in their body is different than anyone else. Because they have always felt the way they do, the deficits just feel normal. They know that certain situations, fabrics, sounds or foods cause them irritation, but they subconsciously believe that everyone else must have the same problem and are better at dealing with the irritation. Those other classmates don't seem to get into trouble.

The children's room in our clinic is large and cheerful, decorated in a child-friendly manner with posters, toys, and games appropriate for children like Ranisha at her kindergarten level. She was an adorable girl. Ranisha was initially very slow to warm up, but once she became comfortable she was a fast-moving target. Her black curls bounced as she charged through the therapy room. She was a blur of motion.

During our initial OT session, Ranisha was allowed to explore items in her own manner. She moved quickly from one activity to another versus more typical play behavior. Toys were interacted with in a surprising manner, such as balls meant for bouncing and throwing were examined closely and turned over and over. Dolls meant to be held, cuddled, and hairstyles or clothing changed were bounced and thrown on the floor. Ranisha sat on a small trampoline and then she bounced upon the chair.

Her initial interactions were very helpful from an OT perspective in understanding Ranisha's way of making sense of her world. Her mother, present during the evaluation, needed to be reassured that Ranisha was not being impolite or disrespectful. Ranisha was merely allowing full rein of her strategies and methods of making sense of her world.

Ranisha responded very quickly to her mother's request for her to say "please," "thank you," and to be respectful. She tried to display the correct behaviors when asked to do so. It became clear that both Ranisha and her mother had had a great deal of practice in curbing Ranisha's behavior. Ranisha seemed very compliant toward her mother's one and two word reminders regarding acceptable behavior.

The cost of Ranisha attending to these socially acceptable and mother-driven cues, however, resulted in reduced productive and organized behaviors on Ranisha's part. For example, when Ranisha's mother imposed the structure of putting one toy away before getting another and to ask before touching, Ranisha dropped to the floor and burst into tears.

Perhaps it was Ranisha's mother's life experiences that led her to believe that this tearful behavior was manipulative on her daughter's part and that it demonstrated disrespect of the adults in the room. As her occupational therapist, however, I viewed her tears from a sensory perspective. As Ranisha absorbed so many new things in our clinic at once, her internal chaos intensified. In that moment her ability to also comply with her mother's rule was overwhelmed, and instantly resulted in Ranisha crying on the floor.

From my perspective, Ranisha was familiarizing herself with the clinical environment, such as the toys and the activities, the personnel, and the new sounds and smells. Ranisha appeared to be working very hard to process the varied experiences offered in this large room. Ranisha's well-meaning mother was also busy processing the new setting together with her daughter's seemingly scattered behavior. Regardless of how things appeared, each of us had our own motives. Ranisha just wanted to touch the toys, her mother wanted her daughter to use manners, and I was aiming to understand the context of Ranisha's chaotic behavior.

To me, her behavior clearly displayed the status of her sensory system* and her manner of acquiring knowledge, in a nut shell, her manner of learning.

Ranisha was trying very hard to please her mother. Sadly, the subtle pressure of her mother's expectations resulted in less appropriate behavior and reduced self-esteem. She didn't want to be bad, and the harder she tried to meet her mother's expectations, the worse her behavior became. When parents understand what is causing the behavior and what they can do to help their unique learner move away from chaos, they can more easily adapt their parenting style to the situation at hand. In this same manner, teachers can expand their approach and reach more unique learners even in a larger classroom environment.

Ranisha didn't want to be thought of as behaving badly, nor did adult Lynette. Lynette was having a similar problem within her working world. Her co-workers were becoming much less tolerant of her behavior. Lynette was functioning in her own paradigm and those in her work place were operating from an extremely different perspective. Lynette's paradigm was one of being the victim and that everyone was just picking on her. However, her co-workers interpreted Lynette's inability to manage her time and complete her tasks as a lack of interest in her job and a lack of respect toward them.

Lynette believed that she was applying herself fully to her job. Those around her were unable to value her contributions because they were overwhelmed by their frustration regarding her lack of reliability and trustworthiness. Through Lynette's denial of her own responsibility, she was unable to see her impact on those around her. Resentment built in the workplace as Lynette's team members were required to do Lynette's work. No pleasantries, flattering remarks, and gentle humor provided by Lynette could dissuade her colleagues from their growing resentment.

* See Glossary for definition

As an adult receiving OT, Lynette was actively involved in setting goals and prioritizing her concerns. We mutually elected to begin working on her "weird sense of touch." Of all of Lynette's problems, her hypersensitivity to touch was the least threatening for her to discuss during the initial phases of OT. Beginning in an area where a person is most comfortable, regardless of the person's age, will always result in more successful outcomes.

Lynette's anti-hypersensitivity program began with a basic explanation about how the tactile nerves work with the rest of the nerves. She was taught that the connection between the skin and all the nerves throughout the body has far-reaching implications for physical and, therefore, emotional security. Picture a skin-to-brain connection so that calming and soothing the skin calms the brain.

We started each session with a scientific discussion. Lynette learned the basics in neuroanatomy* and neurophysiology*. We read research regarding how the experience of touch is essential to our normal growth and development. The experience of touch can best be explained by considering its two primary pathways.

One pathway connects to a startle-like, fight or flight stress reaction*. Touch traveling on this pathway to the brain can be observed in an unexpected touch, such as creeping up behind an individual and grabbing their shoulders. "Boo!"

The other nerve pathway for touch to reach the brain is by integration of that tactile nerve delivering the touch sensation with other sensory experiences. The familiar and welcome touch of your mother's hug is blended with other data and memories. It is processed in a more complex way, in the higher brain centers (including the motor cortex*). The processing and discriminating aspect of this sense of touch results in a distinct recognition: "this is my mother's touch." It is more connected with cognition (such as memory) than the previously described primal fight or flight touch.

* See Glossary for definition

Understanding these two different presentations of touch, Lynette was asked to identify when and what kind of touch was unwelcome. It was easy for her. She described extreme difficulty wearing clothes of non-natural fibers or clothing that had tags on the inside. Although the tag may be of natural cloth, the sewing thread can frequently be a clear synthetic and, to Lynette, scratchy! The seam on the toe portion of her sock was intolerable and collars or sweaters that rubbed against her neck were a source of great distraction.

Tolerance to clothing material varied due to circumstances unknown to Lynette. Lynette could find herself at work in the middle of the afternoon and suddenly find the texture of her blouse to be highly irritating and too distracting. She was unable to filter out the discomfort. Her ability to concentrate would diminish, and it would soon become the primary focus of her attention. Frequently, she would use her break time to go home and change. Reducing this sensitivity through OT was important to her ability to keep her job.

Lynette found textures of her clothing to be intolerable on some days and "no big deal" on other days. Lynette's sense of touch needed to be considered in terms of other mechanisms involved. The sense of touch does not function in isolation. Sometimes Lynette was sensitive to touch and sometimes not. The experience of touch melds with all the other sensations that the brain processes. It's just one aspect of our sensory system. One sensation affects, integrates, or melds with another. Loud noise may sound like screeching when combined with itchy clothing. The sound, the itch…one thing compounds the other. Our sensory system is very complex.

In school we are taught that there are five human senses: taste, touch, smell, sight, and hearing. During our childhood education, we were not usually informed of two other very important sensory systems: the ability to feel gravity operating on our body that is known as the vestibular system,* and the ability to precisely move our joints and muscles, known as the proprioceptive system*. When any of these sensory systems are not functioning properly, there will be a corresponding difficulty in learning behavior.

People who have trouble touching certain textures also can have trouble listening to certain sounds. In other words, many individuals with tactile hypersensitivity* also have auditory sensitivity*. The tactile and auditory sensory systems have very close origins. Old Western movies show horse-riding heroes tracking the band of robbers by placing an ear on the ground to sense the vibration of the ground under the pounding of horses' hooves. Vibration is a form of touch and registers within the tactile sensory system. Feeling or hearing the vibration of the running horses through the ground allowed the hero time to catch the bad guys. An exaggeration, perhaps, but we do perceive sound through the physical vibration of sound waves.

Lynette described herself to be hypersensitive to certain textures and materials, as well as certain sounds and tones of voice. She described an incident with her supervisor when she had arrived late, missing a client meeting. When the supervisor requested an explanation, Lynette recalled that her breathing pattern changed, her stomach became uncomfortable, and her clothing became irritable. This sudden awareness of these inconvenient physiologic changes resulted in her throat muscles tightening and difficulty speaking. She felt so "stressed" by her supervisor's tone of voice that she forgot the series of events contributing to her reason for being late. "I don't know" was her response. Unfortunately, Lynette still could not see what the big deal was.

A lack of connection between a unique learner's own behavior and the expectations of those around is not uncommon. It can cause great difficulty for unique learners to try to adapt to the subtle rules within a complex social or work situation. With maturity, the cultural pressure to conform to social norms increases. These expectations for behavior can collide with a unique learner's need to process information in their own unique way.

During Ranisha's second appointment, she clearly demonstrated her own way of processing information. She ran into the clinic in such a way that the door hit the wall in a loud manner, and the doorknob impression is still there! She ran through the lobby and up the stairs to the administrative office. Her mother was shocked and she expressed verbal outrage at her daughter for nearly colliding with another patient.

Perhaps, I considered, Ranisha was attempting to relieve any fears or anxieties regarding the physical space that she had come to visit once again. My interpretation was more aligned with Ranisha's. I wanted to support her in her desire to understand the exact physical layout of the two-story clinic. Her mother felt she needed to "show proper manners." Manners, for her mother, were of utmost importance. It was a loving effort to keep her safe.

Ranisha and I toured through the clinic, upstairs and downstairs, the gym, and all the individual treatment rooms. Together, we demystified the space that Ranisha would come to visit on a regular basis. She was re-oriented to the pediatric room with explanations for each item: "These are the dolls you played with." "These are the balls that ended up over here." "This is the trampoline that you sat on and this is the chair you jumped on. Today let's try jumping only on the trampoline." The goal was to help Ranisha feel comfortable within her physical space.

Ranisha's mother remained concerned regarding Ranisha's poor behavior. This "erratic behavior" was the primary reason she was having Ranisha attend clinical OT. Prior to contacting our office, Ranisha had seen the family doctor who agreed that OT might be a way to help Ranisha settle down. She had provided Ranisha with a diagnosis of ADHD and her mother immediately went online and looked up the definition on Wikipedia.org, which stated, "Attention deficit hyperactivity disorder is a developmental neuropsychiatric disorder in which there are significant problems with executive function that cause attention deficits, hyperactivity or impulsiveness, which is not appropriate for the person's age." Developmental neuropsychiatric disorder sounds confusing. It's an official way of saying that some of the brain and nervous system building blocks don't properly communicate to each other, resulting in chaotic or dysfunctional behavior.

As I had experienced twice, one of Ranisha's most overt dysfunctional behaviors was her way of entering a new place, like my clinic. Ranisha's brain was not processing relevant and timely information about the world around her. Each new setting was presented to Ranisha's brain as a clean slate. Ranisha seemed to need to physically explore and demystify the environment as if no prior experience existed. Ranisha's mother described that in an unfamiliar house during a birthday party, her daughter would move from one item in the room to another and one room to the next almost in an obligatory nature. She looked as though she had never been in a bedroom, a living room, or in a house at all before.

So, let's look at why Ranisha acts this way. The answer is similar to why you pick up, turn over, and quickly move on to the next item in a souvenir shop. Imagine that the colorful shop is in a very far-away city and you are fascinated by the trinkets. For you, the items are unfamiliar and require more than just a cursory visual inspection. The items are so unique that you must feel the weight of them in your hand, manipulate them to under-stand their physical characteristics, including height, width, and depth, and to sense the texture.

Some people even bring them closer, to smell. A small hand-woven native basket may have a hint of sage or lemongrass. A pink candle may smell like grapefruit. We explore these items and they hold our attention relative to other items in the souvenir shop. The crystal paperweight may hold our attention until an authentic wall hanging piques our interest. Goodbye paperweight, hello magnificent wall hanging. Each item competing for your attention and each item's ability to hold your attention is based on their proximity to you and their relevance to you.

Ranisha, too, feels compelled to interact with everything all at once. On the other hand, one would think that by now she has become familiar enough with everyday toys and objects as well as the standard layout of a house or office environment. Surely, one wonders, she has been taught the correct manners upon entering such an environment.

So, what's going on? Why can't Ranisha go into a new place without physically interacting with everything, putting stuff everywhere, and doing so in a very, very quick manner? Surely, Ranisha could sit still, look, not run, and not touch.

Let's examine the developmental prerequisites to do just that. To begin with, let's look at what is required for Ranisha to sit still. Sitting still or sitting quietly involves feeling gravity acting on your body and finding the point of your balance in which sitting can be successful. The vestibular system allows you to feel gravity and respond to it. A dysfunctional vestibular system could mean that you lean excessively when sitting, even leaning so much that you could fall out of the chair.

Imagine you are that child who has difficulty feeling gravity operate on your body because your vestibular system is dysfunctional. For whichever of the hundreds of legitimate reasons why this may happen, you probably wouldn't actually fall over because, just in time, your muscles and joints would make the correct adjustments and keep you upright. But it takes effort!

The proprioceptive system allows you to feel your joints and muscles move. It allows you to grade the strength and alter the speed of your movement. The proprioceptive system is responsible for the background, ongoing ability of the muscles and joints to act correctly and to keep you upright when you need to be upright. Your tactile system* allows you to feel the edge of the chair.

For Ranisha, her vestibular, proprioceptive and tactile (VPT) systems were not communicating well with the rest of her sensory system. Watching her run, and remember you are in detective mode now, you would see that each step she places is preventing her from falling forward. Her run is a self-controlled fall-prevention strategy. Deprive her of this speed by saying, "Ranisha, slow down!" and you'll see her misstep. She will need to widen her feet to increase her base of support in an attempt to decrease her chance of falling and hang onto the walls and the furniture with her hands. "Get your hands off the wall!" says Ranisha's mom. "But I need them there," says Ranisha's brain.

Being a detective is hard. Clues are tricky to spot. Watch as Ranisha goes up and down the stairs in a fashion that looks every bit as though she's fooling around unsafely on the staircase. However, if you really look, she is not fooling around at all. She is utilizing her only strategy and is actually exerting a fair bit of effort to do so. She holds one railing with both hands and allows her foot to slide over the leading edge of the step with a slide, bounce, slide, bounce manner. She must hang on to the stair railing and hope it is strong enough to support her.

Ranisha's dysfunctional VPT systems won't let her plan her movements to correctly descend stairs. Her dysfunctional vestibular system interrupts her ability to accurately detect gravity operating on her physical vessel. Ranisha's dysfunctional proprioceptive system is not allowing her to feel the correct response needed by her joints and muscles and her tactile system is not allowing her to sort out and order the information coming into her brain.

Through sheer perseverance and bravery, Ranisha continues to interact with the world. When it comes to living with compromised VPT systems, nothing is effortless. While other children Ranisha's age have shifted their VPT sensory awareness to a more background part of their brain, Ranisha continues to process this information in a very conscious manner. Compensatory strategies to overcome deficiencies in the VPT systems are very strenuous and they can highjack large portions of the brain. Brain real estate is costly. As a result, unique learners feel fatigued a lot of the time.

So don't judge Ranisha until you've walked in her shoes. She is doing the best job she can to gain information from her world through her limited data collection system. What Ranisha has in spades is a highly developed cognitive memory. She's had to because her body doesn't appropriately intuit gravity, movement, and touch. Ranisha must store loads of trial and error data in her mind. Her cognitive memory and her level of intelligence far exceed her years. Ranisha is a very smart child. In fact, when the circumstances are perfect, people like Lynette and Ranisha appear to have no difficulties whatsoever.

Someone with a well-functioning VPT can securely enter a new environment, such as an office environment, knowing they have the tools and ability to process that new space. In a fraction of a second, the person with the well-functioning VPT can determine that "I know that this is a door knob; it must be turned and not pushed like the glass doors at the bank. Once I enter the door, I know this is the kind of place that will have chairs to sit on. I know I am capable of navigating to a chair and I know how to sit without falling."

Ranisha doesn't know any of this information about managing in a new place with certainty. It would be great if someone could give her a heads-up before entering. Ranisha's mother was encouraged to do just this. She would stop in a safe place six to ten feet before entering a new environment. Her mother would crouch down and give Ranisha the play-by-play on what was going to occur once they walked through the door.

Mom would say, "Through that door there will be a room with chairs that other people will be sitting quietly on. We'll go in and sit quietly, too, and then we'll decide the next step together. By the way, this is a place where you must tell your legs to walk; don't let them run. It doesn't work so well to run. You'll see that all the other people have figured that out. So they will be walking and not running, just like you." Mom would, in essence, provide the information that a normally functioning VPT would provide. Usually three or four tips would be all that was needed.

By pausing and giving Ranisha these helpful, accurate, and gentle instructions her mother was also taking a moment to calmly remind herself that this task could be difficult for Ranisha. It seemed to help her mother prepare mentally and emotionally for whatever might happen next.

This approach worked well because it supported a behavior and life skill in which Ranisha could build upon. She was helped to become independent in learning to pause and consider the task prior to just diving in. Not only did it offer Ranisha important information to support her long-term learning, but it also provided a sense of emotional security. Ranisha felt that her mother was on her side, which made a big difference in her own self-confidence. Both Ranisha and her mother preferred this strategy to the past "Stop when I tell you to stop!" yelling strategy.

Ranisha learned that different operating instructions were required for her body in different places. Over time, categories were developed. The physical operating instructions of her body in a grocery store were different from in a parking lot. She began to see that what you do and how you move are different in an empty playground than when crossing the street. Seeing other children swinging on a swing set requires maintaining a safe distance away from the swings in order to avoid getting accidentally walloped by a swinging child. By developing categories, the adult can help the unique learner connect the current experience with something they have already experienced.

Ranisha's parents were taught not to assume anything. Trying to be in detective mode as much as possible, Ranisha's mother planned community outings with the sole agenda of Ranisha learning safe and appropriate behavior in specific circumstances. Ranisha was asked to draw a picture of each of these places in order to help her remember. The pictures allowed her experiences to be generalized, something that happens naturally in a typical learner. Because the pictures created categories of experience, her mother could say, "We're now going to visit my friend who's ill. It will be a little like going to the library where you must use a quiet voice and like going to a store where you can't touch. I know she has a backyard where children who like to run, jump and play can have quite a bit of fun. So let's start out with the 'library quiet' and the 'store don't touch' body and then we'll see the 'play, play, play' backyard and let your body have fun doing that."

As an adult, you have received this kind of coaching before many times yourself. Perhaps the second time your friend took you fishing she reminded you of the correct manner to set the hook and handle the reel to prevent making a rat's nest of the line. Maybe the fourth or fifth time you took a yoga class, the instructor reminded you of what arm and leg positions were needed for downward facing dog. He patiently helped you recall the exact hand posture on the floor, thumbs facing each other, index fingers forward, stretched space between each finger. You are relieved when these people help you without assuming that you already know, or judging you for not recalling the steps perfectly.

While Ranisha's parents were learning how to support Ranisha's VPT systems, the OT program aimed to facilitate development of these vital sensory systems. She needed an individualized program to work on vestibular, proprioceptive and tactile sensory processing* and it had to be fun!

The vestibular system requires exercise and movement that promote a feeling of the gravitational pull of Earth's surface when the individual is in different postures: performing summersaults, rolling down a hill, using a swing set, crawling, crab walking*, yoga, karate, swimming, riding horseback, and any other activity that changes the person's relationship with gravity. The focus must be on the process and not the outcome. Avoiding competitiveness is imperative.

The proprioceptive system needs activities that help develop a strong awareness of the body and the limbs in various positions. The brain can really feel the body even better when there is a little weight or a little resistance. Weight acting on the muscles and joints helps the proprioceptive system and helps coordinated movement. Games and activities that stimulate a person's proprioceptive system are outlined in the "Strategies to Try" section at the end of this chapter.

The tactile system can be facilitated by a brushing program* where a standard scrub brush is gently moved over the surface of the skin of the arms and legs. In addition to a brushing program, allowing the child's hands to interact with various textures and materials is very helpful for developing the tactile system. Various textures of materials should be introduced and changed frequently (feeling the dirt by gardening in the springtime, collecting and tracing crunchy leaves in the fall). Ideas to develop tactile processing are presented in the "Strategies to Try" section at the end of this chapter.

In Ranisha's case, her fast pace of activity, sense of busyness and her extreme shifts in mood, as well as her overly dramatic behaviors, could all be seen as an extension of poorly operating VPT sensory systems. Adult Lynette needed coherent behavior to

* See Glossary for definition

function better at work. Although tactile and auditory sensitivity were the initial problems for which Lynette sought out OT intervention, it appeared that these issues tended to occur when poor self-regulation* was present.

Self-regulation refers to the life skill of independently controlling your own moods, behaviors, and actions. Good self-regulation leads toward a coherent response to the demands of everyday life. Good self-regulation is an optimal strategy for living in this complex world. Poor self-regulation leads to a less productive and a more chaotic approach to the world. Mood fluctuations and the concept of self-regulation have become a big concern to parents and teachers trying to help unique learners.

To understand self-regulation, it is important to understand the manner in which the brain can be revved up and how it can be slowed down. In chapter one, you were introduced to the brain's job of balancing the quantity of the incoming and outgoing information. In addition to this function, the brain can also regulate* the quality of that information. The quality of data is fine-tuned by inhibitory* and facilitatory* signals. The brain sends out signals that hinder, or inhibit, the flow of messages. The inhibited brain response can appropriately slow down the child. When the brain sends out a facilitatory signal, a bias toward being facilitated, sped up and excited tends to be the mood/mode of the individual. Being facilitated (excited) is the opposite of being inhibited (slowed down).

Modulation* is the brain's ability to self-organize or self-regulate* the appropriate inhibition or facilitatory response. The brain modulates itself by increasing the energy of certain messages and reducing the energies of others in a similar way that we control the sound (the energy) coming out of a speaker by turning the volume up or down. This modulation can be also referred to as regulation*.

* See Glossary for definition

Some students, like Ranisha, lean toward a facilitated nervous system. Decades ago, these students would have been termed "hyper." Students that demonstrate signs and symptoms consistent with ADHD will frequently have tense muscles and their voices will hold excitement and urgency. These students look awake, alert, and full of energy. The aim in an OT program for students like Ranisha would be to balance their naturally facilitated state with therapeutic inhibitory methods. In other words, for reducing hyperactivity, occupational therapists use techniques that calm the nervous system. We want to foster a balanced and middle of the road state of mind. To self-regulate successfully, one must independently achieve this optimal learning-ready state of mind.

In contrast to a facilitated state, students in a more inhibitory state look generally low in activity participation. They may seem tuned out, slowed down, and reticent to the point of defiant. For this more shut down unique learner, the OT aim would be to balance the student's natural inhibitory state with therapeutic facilitatory methods. Again, the overall goal is to achieve a balanced state.

Unique learners can have various combinations of circumstances when their hyperactivity is mixed with periods of lethargy. Some children have a tendency toward a facilitatory response in certain situations and in other situations the overall bias is one of a more inhibitory response. In speaking to her teacher, some days Ranisha would arrive at school already in a super excitable mode. Other days she would arrive in an inhibitory or shut down mode.

Ranisha's teacher became very astute at identifying Ranisha's (and many of the other students') background energy level. She began to vary the introduction of the daily curriculum in a manner that eased the wild-eyed students and woke up any sleepy-heads. Her teacher quickly learned that Ranisha seemed to become very stirred up and over-stimulated* when she was approached in a

* See Glossary for definition

fast and energetic manner. Ranisha calmed down when given less direct eye contact and a softer and more general expectation that she should participate with the class.

Ranisha's parents became good detectives. They developed an awareness of the activities that were arousing for her, such as loud noises, bright lights, and entering unknown spaces, especially without a perceived game plan. It also became apparent to Ranisha's parents that low lights, low sounds, consistent and unvarying warm temperatures were calming for Ranisha. This is true for many unique learners.

When Ranisha was too excited, they would employ calming strategies. Body compression exercises (also known as squeezes*) and the use of a weighted blanket* helped her calm and refocus after school. When Ranisha was too lethargic and slowed down, they would employ arousal strategies. In this way, Ranisha's level of participation and her moods could be better regulated. Appropriate modulation can reduce the extremes of behavior.

Because Ranisha was usually too excited and more often in a highly facilitated mode (versus a more shut down and inhibited mode), Ranisha's parents used calm-down, inhibitory methods for her home program. Ranisha's calm-down program is depicted in the "Strategies to Try" section at the end of this chapter.

Eventually, Ranisha was encouraged to become self-aware of these strategies and learned to calm herself down or rev herself up appropriately. As Ranisha demonstrated reduced meltdown and other behavioral extremes, she had more self-control. The poor choices that had become automatic as well as other inappropriate behaviors and habits occurred less often and became less intense in nature.

When considering adults with ADHD, the strategies and exercises have a similar emphasis as childhood ADHD intervention. For Lynette, her adult OT program would shift emphasis based on

* See Glossary for definition

her response to treatment. For example, after focusing on tactile hypersensitivity, Lynette's primary OT intervention was changed to help develop self-awareness of her moods and behavior swings. Just like Ranisha, she had certain events and triggers causing facilitated behaviors and others causing slowed down behaviors.

Just like Ranisha, Lynette learned to employ calming (inhibitory) behaviors when she was overstimulated. When she was too slowed down, she employed stimulating (facilitating) behaviors. It was important for Lynette to learn how to modulate her own behavior. Lynette needed to minimize poor work performance and keep her job!

Ranisha's parents became more and more hopeful as the strategies they were using began helping their daughter be more quiet and calm. The inhibitory strategies that her parents used made a noticeable difference in her ability to focus. Ranisha's parents, like all parents, wanted their child's potential to be fully realized. They were committed to helping their daughter in every way possible so she could experience success in school and in life.

As an adult, Lynette needed to learn how to use her brain more effectively, to think more clearly with less fatigue. Organizing her brain involved proper integration of the entire sensory system. Learning to organize her brain through multi-sensory stimulation helped Lynette's brain function better. Lynette learned best when accessing as many sensory systems as possible.

For all of us, including unique learners like Ranisha and Lynette, it is important to remember that the brain prefers to maintain a physiologic state that allows for optimal functioning, coherent thinking and organized behavior. Unfortunately, the brain and sensory system can become biased toward less coherence, resulting in a sense of disconnect and erratic behavior. In a nutshell, the brain can move from coherence to chaos and back again.

Recognizing the continuum from chaos to coherence is imperative. Recognizing these states becomes important in optimizing self-regulation for learning readiness behaviors*. With strategies to promote a blend of calmness with alertness, an individual can enjoy the full range of human experiences. In OT, Lynette started remembering to pay bills, she developed skills to hold down full-time employment, and juggling parenting duties became easier for her. Ranisha discovered that rocking in the kitchen rocking chair right after school while her mom made her a healthy snack was the exact thing she needed to refresh herself. Then she could engage in 20 minutes of school reading followed by a break* that included outdoor activities.

While facilitating an optimal brain mode is crucial for helping those with hyperactivity, it is also very helpful for individuals with autism* and for slow-to-warm-up, shy and reticent students as well. While this chapter discussed Ranisha's and Lynette's hyperactive behavior, in the next chapter we will focus on what the adult can do to help the autistic unique learner move from chaos to coherence. This is an important strategy that applies for many unique learners. The reader will see that overlapping strategies are presented in working with children with hyperactivity (ADHD), with coordination problems, with autism spectrum disorder (ASD)*, with trouble reading and trouble writing. Chapter four presents learning solutions for the population of students on the autism spectrum. But first, please see the "Strategies to Try" section below for immediate solutions for the hyperactive child or adult.

　　　　　　　　　　* See Glossary for definition

STRATEGIES TO TRY

IF your child or student has difficulty entering a new space, such as a grocery store, doctor's office, or classroom,

THEN try to give your child a heads-up on what to expect just before entering the new environment. Provide three or four simple suggestions, such as the need to walk and not run, to speak in a quiet voice, and any other relevant behaviors that you know your child can achieve. Sometimes it is helpful to visit places merely to practice these behaviors. Make it fun and share the joy of your mutual success together.

IF your child or student has difficult attending and if they seem distracted and just can't concentrate,

THEN try activities that stimulate the sensory system* to help give the brain more input for learning and for playing. The specific sensory activities in this chapter involve the VPT systems. Try one or two activities every day:

The vestibular system requires a diet of feeling the gravitational pull of the earth's surface in a variety of different postures. Summersaults, rolling down a hill, using a swing set, crawling, crab walking, yoga, karate, swimming, riding horse-back, and any activity that changes the person's relationship with gravity (and is, preferably,

* See Glossary for definition

noncompetitive) can help facilitate the vestibular system. The focus must be on the process of the activity and not the outcome. Avoiding competitiveness is important because the focus is sensory integration,* not winning or losing.

The proprioceptive system needs activities that help develop a strong awareness of the body and the limbs in various positions. The brain can really feel the body even better when there is a little weight or a little resistance. Weight acting on the muscles and joints stimulates the proprioceptive system and helps coordinate movement. The fun imaginary game of playing marching band with pounding feet is great. Marching causes weight and resistance to transmit through the joints of the legs. The weight and resistance facilitate the proprioceptors. Helping with heavy chores is also terrific. Pushing or carrying something heavy applies weight through the arms and through the legs. Pushups, standing wall pressups, seated chair pressups, crossing the arms and hugging or squeezing the torso, as well as safely catching and tossing a weighted beanbag, all facilitate the proprioceptors.

The tactile system can be facilitated by a brushing program where a standard scrub brush is gently moved over the surface of the skin of the arms and legs. In addition to a brushing program, allow the hands to interact with various textures and materials, such as play dough, paper mache, and finger painting. Allowing a child to help perform baking and gardening tasks, as well as teaching a child the correct use of tools, all assist with tactile processing. The child must grasp the tool differently depending on the task.

IF your child seems to be too sped up, either mentally or physically, and you are at home,

THEN try to calm them down by using these calm-down strategies, but adapt them to your child's needs:

Calm their mood by wrapping your child in a soft blanket, dim the lights, use a calm and steady low voice, and introduce a slow and rhythmic rocking. Continue for three to five minutes or until you see a relaxation response begin to appear.

Apply gentle and slow squeezes* to the child's body. Also, brushing can be helpful with the use of a standard scrub brush and moving the brush very slowly over the surface of the arms and the legs, avoiding any brushing that may go against the hairs on the skin. Brushing can be done every two hours in order to minimize periods of extreme hyperactivity.

———————

IF your child seems to be too sped up and you are not at home or if you are a teacher in a classroom,

THEN "calm the brain" by pushing gently and slowly on the small joints of the fingers and applying circumferential pressure or gentle hugs along the length of the arm, compress and gently squish the hand, and even apply squeezes or "head hugs" to the head. Watch your child's facial expressions. Usually they enjoy it so much that they raise their arm and offer it to you in hope that you will perform compression exercises.

———————

IF your child is irritated by clothing, tags, socks, and other fabrics that touch their skin,

THEN facilitate a brushing program where a standard soft scrub brush (such as a nail brush) is gently moved over the surface of the skin of the arms and the legs. Periodically change the texture of the brush to prevent the skin from accommodating to the stimulation. Allow your child the opportunity to perform this brushing program on themselves. Encourage walking barefoot on a tactile obstacle course (different textured bathmats) arranged in an appealing, tricky course.

—————

IF your child or student has difficulty controlling their emotions and seems to lose their temper too easily or shuts down and stops participating altogether,

THEN help them better regulate* their sudden change in mood by becoming aware of what triggers the high-energy anger and the low-energy shutdown. High-energy anger is a facilitated*, excited, sped-up characteristic of the brain. Low-energy shutdown is an inhibited, slowed-down characteristic of the brain. When you look at your child's world from a perspective of things that can either speed them up mood-wise or slow your child down, you will become their student. They will teach you what revs them up and what slows them down.

When you assume a nonjudgmental detective role, you will begin to see patterns in your child's behaviors. So when your child is too high energy, encourage participation in things that calm the child down. When your child is too low energy, encourage participation in things that you have observed to cause your child to speed up and become excited about.

***

IF your child or student has difficulty getting things done within a reasonable timeframe, either completing them too quickly or too slowly,

THEN help your child experience how long simple tasks take to complete by using a clock or a timer. Choose a few tasks that they are already successful at completing and let them time themselves. You can say, "When you listen to your favorite song it takes three minutes. That's the same time it takes to wash your hands and brush your teeth before school."

CHAPTER FOUR

THE AUTISM SPECTRUM: OPTIMIZE THE ENVIRONMENT

Children streamed into the classroom, laughing and talking in loud voices. Bright artwork made by the second-grade students covered the walls. In fact, what wall space wasn't covered with art was filled with posters illustrating the second-grade curriculum. The students themselves were a jumble of color and movement as they hung up their jackets and made their way to their seats. Silence began to creep across the room as the students observed their teacher on her knees peering under one of the work tables. Their new classmate, David, was under the table, keeping out of reach of the teacher as she tried in vain to snag his clothing to pull him out.

Ms. Hall raised her head from under the table and directed the students to sit down and begin reading. To the adult helper in the back of the classroom, her frustration was evident. The students opened their books, but kept peeking with curiosity at the scene in the middle of the classroom. The silence was punctuated with occasional outbursts of yelling from David and murmurs from the teacher. Finally, the teacher announced that she was going to go to the phone to call his mother. She moved away from the table, which brought the boy out from under the table where he tried to pull the phone from the teacher's hand.

The adult helper shook her head. "If my child ever acted like that I would take away every privilege they had," she thought to herself. "What a brat!"

Disruptive and upsetting, the incident passed when David and a friendly staff member went to a nearby quiet spot. A couple of responsible second-grade "buddies" went along to help calm David down. Back in the classroom, the adult helper questioned the teacher indignantly. The teacher's response came as a surprise. This normal looking boy was autistic. He had been diagnosed with autism spectrum disorder (ASD)*. David's behavior was not due to bratty-ness. He didn't know how else to deal with his reactions to this environment. David was a unique learner and had his own way of learning.

This type of scene plays out in schools across the country for students on the autism spectrum. Their parents and teachers struggle daily with routines and activities that, for other students, offer not even the slightest difficulty. Because children with autism can appear normal in every way except behaviorally, people around them have high expectations of their performance. They appear similar to their peers and are mistakenly assumed to function and behave just like those around them. Parents and school administrators often feel at odds with one another over how to best meet the needs of the individual student, the classroom, and the school as a whole. This challenge is exponentially increased with a unique learner.

Autism is a disorder that has a huge range of characteristics. Doctors will sometimes refer to these individuals as "on the spectrum." The doctors mean that the child has behaviors that fall within a cluster of problems. The chief signs of "autism" are social isolation, lack of eye contact, poor language skills, and an absence of understanding another person's perspective. The term

* See Glossary for definition

autism is derived from a Greek word that means "self." The name suggests the most obvious feature of autism: withdrawal from social interaction. Children on the autism spectrum may have difficulty relating to people and things. Their rate of development may be skewed and their ability to process sensations and to perceive and understand events can be dysfunctional. They may have difficulty communicating and they may have difficulty moving in a balanced, functional, and typical fashion. Hand flapping, like air drying wet hands, can also be associated with ASD.

Complex verbal communication with other people can be a problem. The individual with ASD tends to interpret language very literally. For example, in the statement "I was trying to do my homework, but I hit a brick wall," a person with autism may hear this statement as if the speaker actually physically hit a brick wall. "Wow! That must have hurt." What was meant, and the surprising literal interpretation made by the person with ASD, often confounds further conversation and leads to difficulty establishing meaningful relationships.

Children and adults on the autism spectrum may differ from the more typical population by how they connect with people and how they relate to things. In some cases, lack of eye contact and lack of speaking skills cause profound isolation. An object or a toy may not be used in a typical manner. It could be thrown, spun, flicked at, or disassembled rather than used for the express purpose of the toy. One of my young patients liked to disassemble the vacuum. He usually did it correctly.

Students on the autism spectrum also show difficulty reproducing other people's actions. Mimicking others is how many of us learn to do new things. The inability to watch and learn from others results in a significant learning challenge for our current educational model that is very dependent on the teacher providing demonstrations.

Teachers and parents alike feel helpless when trying to show their child a new skill. One parent described how difficult it was to show his 14-year-old son how to change a flat tire on his bike. Toilet training, using an eating utensil, or even handing in homework to the correct homework stack can all be very difficult skills to teach a child with ASD. Because learning by mimicking for most of us is subconscious, we are not aware that students with ASD must learn differently.

Children and adults on the autism spectrum with the same diagnosis can be very, very different from one individual to the next. Though all people who fall within the autism spectrum are diagnosed with "autism spectrum disorder" (ASD), I want to help make clear that ASD has many degrees of severity. In this chapter, three students will be introduced that depict a range of difficulties. David is the second-grade student already introduced in Ms. Hall's class. He functions within a general education classroom with some irregularities in his behavior. Logan is a high school student and also functions in a general education curriculum environment. Cara will be the third student depicted in this chapter. She is more severely impacted by her autism and her schooling takes place in a special day class environment.

David and Logan are similar in their degree of involvement and both students could be considered mild to moderate on the autism spectrum. David is playful and enjoyed by his second-grade peers. Logan is in tenth grade and his peers have become more adult-like. Logan's issues surround the growing feeling of being alone and isolated.

David, back in the second grade classroom, had difficulty following the class structure familiar to his peers. Sometimes he acted in an unusual fashion, such as hiding underneath the tables in the classroom or running to a distant part of the school campus. Though David's parents had few ideas on how to settle him down,

* See Glossary for definition

they were outstanding in their commitment and effort to follow through and help the school do the best job possible for their child.

Two years prior, while in a general education kindergarten classroom, it became clear to David's parents that the demands of a regular school setting were not promoting their son's learning-readiness behaviors. When they found their efforts to home school David were not optimal either, they were anxious to find a solution that would work. David re-entered a public school setting partway through Ms. Hall's second-grade curriculum. His parents had both hope and reservations about enrolling him in a general education curriculum once again.

David quickly became friends with Ms. Hall. She was a very intelligent educator who had recently become an elementary school teacher after many years as a middle school teacher. Though she tended to draw a "hard line" in terms of classroom behaviors, her approach was targeted on encouraging the best from her students. She naturally took a detective* approach and, although she had clear expectations for behavior, Ms. Hall remained a non-judgmental observer*. With all her students, Ms. Hall was looking for evidence that said to her, "Brain working here*." She understood the mechanisms of brain biology well enough to understand that through fostering independent problem-solving abilities and a sense of a general curiosity in her students, she could really help them now as well as later in their school life. Ms. Hall wanted to teach her students how to use their brains to their greatest capacity. She tried to understand what kinds of behaviors and actions promoted her students to learn how to learn.

Ms. Hall had no experience with unique learners with ASD. During my observation time in her classroom, she privately shared that she had raised and trained horses all her life. Through this experience, she believed in the power of respectful, nonverbal communication, non-threatening eye contact, and a steady voice.

These very qualities were later identified as the prime reason Ms. Hall was so successful at educating David. Her students were held accountable for behavior respectfully and compassionately. She would calmly communicate fully with any student needing extra help while the rest of the class and the lesson were held at bay. This calm communication helped David, as well as the other students, understand what was expected.

To place David's behavior in context, he had previously been identified as an impulsive student. The impulsivity at a younger age consisted of resistance to the kindergarten class agenda. For example, he refused to sit with the other students on the carpet during circle time and would shriek until he was allowed to use the computer located at the back of the classroom. David was quiet and joyful when playing computer games, so, more often than not, the fatigued kindergarten teacher gave in and allowed extended computer privileges. After all, the teacher had the entire class to consider.

In first grade, David had become a genuine source of distraction to himself and others by somersaulting or spinning within the rows of student desks. Though this was David's attempt to find a steady state for his sensory system*, what you and I might achieve with a deep breath, it was obviously quite disruptive in the classroom.

David required excessive support and attention from the classroom teacher during teaching time. He had a frightening tendency to impulsively run from the classroom, move from his seat on the school bus while the school bus was moving, and interact with his peers in a negative and harmful manner. At this point, David was temporarily removed from his first-grade general education curriculum and began to participate in a home school curriculum. Finally, when David's parents felt he had difficulty focusing while at home, they hoped that Ms. Hall's classroom could finish their son's second-grade education with better success.

* See Glossary for definition

During his first month in Ms. Hall's class, David spent much of his time avoiding participation in activities by crawling underneath the tables and asking to leave the classroom. At circle time, while seated on the carpet, he was seen to place his hand on the head of the child seated in front of him. David would physically pat the child's hair repeatedly until the child moved out of his reach or complained to the teacher. Sometimes his fingers would become entangled in the child's long ponytail and he would inadvertently hurt the classmate in front of him. At other times, he would rock his body side to side so vigorously that he would collide with students to his left and right side. David frequently would thrust his head backward, coming very close to injuring the student sitting behind him on the carpet. Attempts to curb these behaviors resulted in David retreating to a spot underneath the table, avoiding any adult's attempt to reach him. Perhaps more alarming was this student's tendency to elope*.

A full staff meeting was scheduled to address this severe safety concern. Elopement* is a term used by school personnel to describe a student who runs away. David would run to the opposite end of the fenced-in school playground to be far away from his peers instead of moving in the direction of his classroom after recess. At the meeting the school was informed that, on one occasion, David had even run away from his home. Fortunately, David's home was nestled in a very quiet and safe neighborhood. David's father stated, "I was less scared during my time in combat (as an enlisted serviceman) than I was when David went missing!" The school personnel echoed this profound concern.

Despite the seemingly erratic behavior, David's peers genuinely enjoyed his company. His classmates "got" David. This social skill of David's was a very important clue as it suggested that the other children saw something the adults did not see regarding this child's cooperative play interactions. His classmates liked his creative activities and they liked how David made sense of the world. He understood the rules of play and was creative and fun.

Observing how same-age peers interact with a unique learner can be very telling in terms of the student's ability to be understood and to exchange communications in a meaningful and compassionate manner. David's classmates trusted him. They were not deterred by his behaviors, which seemed erratic to the adults in the classroom. Students sought David out for work partners and other activities, an accomplishment in light of his "new student" status. To do this, David must have been incorporating short-term memory to remember the rules of the game, linear sequencing to share at the appropriate time, and adding creativity that children in second grade would characterize as fun. All of these traits indicate average to above-average intelligence and a strong potential for learning.

Through continuing education courses and teacher workshops, the learning readiness behaviors* of students with ASD are better recognized. Teachers are now learning that unique learners, like David, will always have sensory processing* irregularities that require special consideration. Teachers are learning how to create an ideal environment to promote the focused attention of students on the autism spectrum. These teachers employ body language and effective use of voice that assist not just the unique learners; even more typical students achieve improved attention span. Educators are beginning to realize (as Ms. Hall realized through her work with horses) that consistent, steady, and gentle nonverbal communication can be one of the most powerful tools in inspiring a young child to learn, particularly one easily upset and confused, such as David.

Ms. Hall, like many teachers, quickly discovered that the strategies she had been using for her student on the autism spectrum were strategies that helped the general classroom body as well. By embracing the educational needs of the autistic student, many

* See Glossary for definition

teachers have told me that they become better teachers in every aspect of their teaching career.

Ms. Hall's teaching style modeled total acceptance of David by respecting him enough to place the same social expectations on him as the other children in the class. She was as consistent and respectful during her interactions with David as she was with all her students.

Many times, David seemed like a great student. Like many individuals on the autism spectrum, he was highly intelligent. He gradually developed an understanding of the class structure. He was more attentive, looking and listening appropriately. Sometimes, however, David just could not keep it together. Excessive eye contact, prolonged attention, and close physical proximity tipped David's emotional balance and contributed to overstimulation* behaviors. He seemed very much like a young puppy. He became wound up when unfamiliar adults approached him with quick movements, intense eye contact, or excessive sounds and vocalizations. Overly exuberant high-fives with loud clapping and calling out were a big mistake!

David's behavior provided clues to what was and wasn't appropriately happening in his brain and body. A non-judgmental detective would analyze this behavior without making good or bad assumptions and could then recognize that David was having difficulty finding a steady state for his sensory system. David had trouble modulating (or self-regulating*) his mood, behaviors and actions. Finding a better steady state for his irregular behavior would involve "tuning" his energy level, like a dial on a radio, to an optimal level.

David continued to struggle. Gradually, the activities that triggered problem behaviors were identified. Task avoidance, poor social behaviors, hurting others and playground elopement needed to be eliminated. The school staff was very keen to identify and prevent triggers of unacceptable behaviors and to help David become more successful.

Academically related OT* was suggested with the goal of facilitating David's ability to regulate* (or better control) his classroom behaviors and to successfully participate in sustained academic tasks. For a period of time, David was demonstrating a greater frequency and intensity of impulsive actions. David's parents and school team felt that interventions would help promote more "positive learning behaviors*." Strategies were needed to help his ability to focus his thinking and modulate* his moods.

Through an OT observation/evaluation of David over several school days, I wanted to identify the incidents that triggered David's chaotic* behaviors. I was also looking for those activities that could promote calm learning-readiness in David. I wanted to see what caused chaos* and what caused coherence*. The results were surprising.

When David sat under the table, this was viewed as calming and, therefore, a functional activity. He really enjoyed being the student who quickly responded to the teacher's general questions put forth to the class. Answering the teacher's questions while under the table was initially tolerated by Ms. Hall. The teacher began to provide David with more physical space during carpet time and more options during instructional sessions. Additionally, Ms. Hall realized that too much teacher attention would tend to trigger the over-stimulated puppy-like wiggle behaviors that were viewed as disorganizing and non-functional.

Ms. Hall continued to use her detective skills to create her own personal roster of activities that promoted optimal performance in David. She identified what helped and didn't help. She noted that the more often David behaved within the optimal range, the more his negative behaviors decreased. It seemed his impulsive and

* See Glossary for definition

poor behavior, including elopement, was decreasing and he was showing a greater repertoire of age-appropriate activities.

Interacting with his teacher was a preferred activity for David. Ms. Hall was astute in recognizing that the quality of David's responses indicated that he was listening to the lessons and focusing appropriately on the topic. Ms. Hall's focus was always to identify "brain working here." With this focus, she considered David a successful student even when he answered from under the desk. His brain was working in a coherent* fashion. At this initial stage, she was unconcerned that the brain belonged to a child sitting underneath a table rather than on a chair. Ms. Hall was able to use this as a stepping stone to promote David's growth.

Over time, Ms. Hall casually expected David to get out from under the table and move himself closer to the class. Eventually, David was encouraged to respond to the teacher only when he was seated just like his classmates at his desk and chair. After this successful leap in improved behavior, David was then expected to wait his turn and allow other students to offer their responses as well.

She used her voice, tone of speech, and content of language carefully when praising David. Less verbal expression of reward, versus too much praise, seemed to promote his internal motivation and sense of self-satisfaction. David did not respond well to a higher pitched "Nice job!" and "Way to go!" set of platitudes. Ms. Hall felt that encouraging David to learn, based on internal motivation and self-satisfaction, was more functional than David doing something to gain verbal praise from the teacher. For example, the teacher would point out that David needed to color more in a specific location of his sailboat drawing versus offering effusive verbal praise. By suggesting the need for more specific coloring, the powerful internal message to David was "You are capable."

One of the turning points in David's success was when his teacher adopted a break* schedule. The OT evaluation revealed that David required frequent breaks to refresh his ability to focus on his class work. Initially, these breaks needed to be pre-designated and hardwired into the classroom curriculum on a three times per day basis. In addition to these three scheduled breaks, the teacher and other adults in the classroom became attuned to David's early warning signs that could lead to disruptive behavior. When David became less productive and more chaotic in his behavior, an additional break was added to the schedule.

Initially David's breaks needed to be conducted outside of the classroom to not interrupt others. David was taught how to reenter the classroom in a quiet fashion to assist the teacher and other students in their own steady performance. Breaks while in the classroom incorporated directing David toward preferred activities, such as a small squish ball as well various toys and figurines that he enjoyed. Eventually, the use of a timer was employed to identify work cycles and the need for a break. This allowed David to be in charge of initiating and discontinuing his classroom-based breaks. Breaks outside of the classroom were now seldom needed.

In addition to brain-refreshing classroom breaks, other discoveries were made to help modulate David's brain activity. Fidgeting with small toys in his hand appeared to improve David's ability to listen. David was provided with a small ball of resistive putty as a "working toy," something to use when his brain really needed to work. This helped David's brain modulate to an optimal learning-ready* state. The putty was kept on the teacher's desk and Ms. Hall seemed to know the perfect moment that David needed a fidget toy to help him focus. As a "working toy," it was never offered as a reward or removed as a punishment. The fidget was considered a part of David's diet for calmness.

* See Glossary for definition

Because sustained eye contact appeared to overload and cause a disintegration of organized behavior, educators and adults in the classroom were reminded to avoid this stimulus and stay alert to David's tendency to become overloaded. Loud noises were also overstimulating. David was provided with noise cancellation headphones when he participated in the music room with his classmates practicing on the recorder. The use of headphones and other preemptive strategies can help a child's brain stay in a learning-ready state by preventing the inevitable overstimulation from occurring in the first place. For unique learners such as David, this is more than just a school strategy and soon becomes a lifestyle management tool.

David made immediate progress. After just two weeks, only three scheduled breaks each day were needed. David continued to require adult assistance during these breaks to maximize positive learning behaviors. In other words, David was not yet at the stage that he could identify when he needed a break. Nor was he able to use the break time efficiently without adult intervention. The intrinsic belief was that, over time and as David matured, he would be able to recognize his need for a break and take one.

When working with children older than David, it is important to involve them in the discovery process of their own behavioral triggers. These older students can quickly offer solutions once they are aware of the triggers. The process can be made more difficult because the more mature child has often developed a negative opinion of themselves. Along the way, they have also developed equally unproductive coping mechanisms such as task avoidance and anti-social behaviors.

One such unique learner, Logan, was a tenth-grade high school student with a full head of thick, dark, wavy hair. His brown eyes, olive complexion, and a tall physique gave Logan an enviable and attractive appearance. Logan didn't think so. Logan did not like himself. He was old enough to know that his ASD separated him from his peers. He would frequently ask his parents why he could not be "normal." Logan had difficulty relating to his peers and became easily embarrassed, resulting in further isolation. He was quickly frustrated when made to follow complex classroom instructions, such as those needed to correctly complete a science project.

His mother described him as having a short fuse and a quick temper. He was easily angered and acted as though he was always in a bad mood. His eyes were downcast because he had learned to avoid other students who might notice his uncontrolled habit of furtively glancing around. Forcing himself to look downward as he walked through the hall was a coping strategy to avoid "looking strange" to other students. He avoided looking up whenever possible. The more he avoided eye contact, the more fear, anxiety, and sense of aloneness he invoked in himself.

Clearly, Logan's poor self-esteem was compounding the difficulties related to his autism. To add to his concerns, Logan's parents were repeatedly complaining to Logan and his teachers that Logan had sloppy handwriting. They feared he would never progress unless he could write more neatly. Writing neatly seemed pointless to Logan as he was convinced that no one would be interested to read what he wrote. Both parties were making incorrect assumptions.

Cafeteria personnel were concerned about Logan's isolative behavior and it was these caring employees who really initiated the school's involvement. The school staff felt that most of his needs could be met if he would only develop confidence and skill in expressing himself. The school counselor began to see Logan on a bimonthly basis to allow him an opportunity to sort out his social confusions, to express his feelings, and to provide him with a forum to feel reassurance that his school concerns were manageable.

The school counselor was very compassionate toward Logan's unique learning needs. She had received specialized training in autism spectrum disorders. She knew that Logan's challenges, both academically and socially, were typical of many people with autism. For example, Logan wasn't able to observe someone else's action and then reproduce it. He couldn't recall the steps the science teacher demonstrated in the biology lab. He couldn't organize the important details, sequence them, and follow through with actions in a timely fashion. Logan felt that no other student wanted to partner with someone so disorganized.

It took time but as Logan became more comfortable with the counselor, he would often share stories of his day. Some of the stories suggested an almost eccentric preoccupation with trivial stimuli. He would go on at length about an injustice he observed. He was distracted by the material of some of his new clothing that his mother bought him; a flashing exit sign in the gymnasium made it hard for him to listen to the teacher; and the rough undersurface of a desk in the social studies classroom was almost unbearable and almost always created an upset when Logan tried to sit elsewhere and caused another student to move.

To further complicate his school day, Logan had an extreme aversion to certain sounds that seemed to set off alarm bells in his mind for no obvious reason. Some of Logan's poor behavior was triggered by these unexpected loud sounds, such as a loud sneeze. His exaggerated response to the sound of a sneeze led to embarrassment and further disintegration of peer relationships. He was intolerant of prolonged eye contact and this was a real social handicap. He couldn't tolerate the brisk changes in agenda that were a constant part of his high school curriculum. He would become agitated and was unable to stay calm for unscheduled pep rallies, which he dreaded.

With the help of the school staff, Logan became aware of a sense of personal responsibility in choosing how to respond to environmental stimulation on a moment-by-moment basis. Although triggers seemed to happen automatically, he learned to wait it out*. Logan was taught that most negative thought patterns, anger for instance, could trigger a cascade of chemical releases that surge through the brain and body. Recognizing the experience to be biochemical and short-term in nature, Logan developed the skill of waiting it out. He learned that he could choose to allow the surge of chaos to continue, by fueling it with negative thinking, or he could choose to endure its brief journey, resulting in a natural stopping point. In other words, wait it out. The ramification of his choice would either lead to an undesirable event in his brain that caused a surge of stress hormones to circulate repeatedly, causing his thinking to get all locked up, or he could choose a more desirable outcome by waiting it out. Soon he learned to control the upset feelings and to get on with his school work.

Role playing* was employed to assist Logan in learning how to interact with others. When he thought another student was acting in a hostile manner, Logan learned that he could choose to either engage in the other person's anger and perpetuate a trigger of his own negative physiologic cycle, or stay calm and express compassion, thus preventing a chemical burst of anger in his own body. In short, Logan was inspired to think about his own thought process.

Logan also learned to identify his own internal contributors to chaos, such as self-deprecating thoughts. Through the help of the school counselor, he became aware that negative remarks that he directed toward himself promoted a shutdown of his cognitive abilities. For this reason, he also became aware of how to identify when negative thinking was biasing his ability to participate fully in what could be a very joyful series of events and daily activities.

With the knowledge that a feeling of peace and coherence could always be found within him, Logan became more socially daring and began volunteering answers aloud in his classroom. Logan was proud to announce that he had set a goal for himself to raise his hand at least once a day and speak in front of the class. Through this newfound confidence, Logan was able to enjoy more social interactions with peers. He was less isolative at lunchtime and was included in age-appropriate conversations regarding other students' social concerns.

As Logan developed an understanding of his own circumstances, he began to see that other students had their own difficulties. One day while seated at lunch, the classmate next to Logan was speaking to the small group of students surrounding them. Logan was horrified to hear this student describe a story regarding his difficulty with reading and his father's assumption that his reading errors and difficulties meant he was stupid. He told his friends that he thought that everyone believed he was stupid and that he would never read aloud or even raise his hand in a class situation. Logan hadn't suspected that other students had any challenges or struggles. He was surprised to discover that this knowledge provided him with even more confidence and he found himself answering teacher questions more often. He began answering questions aloud to help other students. Soon he overcame his own fear of speaking in front of his classmates.

Logan's science class curriculum introduced him to some of the concepts of right brain and left brain learning*. He expressed a keen interest in this topic. In OT, we worked together to establish a beneficial program that could capitalize on this core interest. Logan tended to favor activities that promoted integration of the right and left brain hemispheres. Often students and patients know what they need once they see their circumstances from a non-judgmental observer perspective. Right brain/left brain* activities were exactly what Logan's sensory-motor system* needed.

Our program consisted of the following three brain-processing skills: crossing the midline*, visual motor tracking,* and spatial awareness* skills. The right brain/left brain processing skills are outlined in the "Strategies to Try" section at the end of this chapter.

* See Glossary for definition

Logan did them with his whole class during PE and when at home between homework assignments.

Eventually, Logan started a small social lunch group that met weekly to practice communication skills and to role play age-appropriate life activities, such as experiencing a job interview. Logan developed this lunch club on his own with the help of his compassionate school teacher. Logan experienced going from self-isolation to helping instigate a club for both himself and his classmates to practice and discuss social behaviors. Concepts such as "Why did he look at me that way?" and "What's wrong with telling the teacher (on him)?" are common areas where these unique learners fall into difficulty and awkwardness in social situations. Appropriate strategies and shared experiences can provide all unique learners with better outcomes.

Logan was considered to be on the mild end of the autism spectrum when tested at his high school. He was able to make great progress through this team approach. More severely in-volved students with autism can make progress, but the positive changes must be viewed in perspective to their level of severity and degree of disability. In their early years, the child and student on the autism spectrum may need quite a bit of help. They have a harder time managing themselves and the world around them.

Cara was one such child. She was severely autistic and her behaviors were difficult to predict or to manage. Cara was a wild child. She had profound difficulty learning at school. Her curric-ulum was individualized and modified. She was placed in a class-room where the teacher was trained in educating students with significant developmental delays. The other adults in the class-room were also specifically trained in teaching autistic students. The classroom had a high ratio of adults to students and it was ideally suited to Cara's unique learning needs. Even within her highly modified curriculum, Cara needed frequent breaks and they needed to occur outside of the classroom due to her disruptive behavior.

Cara's random behaviors could not be anticipated even at the fifth-grade level. Her movements oscillated from fast and furious to complete lethargy and sleepiness. It was not unusual for Cara to whirl around the class all morning and to sleep the entire afternoon session. She had a worrisome behavior of placing non-edible items in her mouth, a behavior the school nurse referred to as "overuse of her oral mechanism."

As the year progressed, the other developmentally delayed students in Cara's classroom became familiar with the step-by-step procedures. For them, the structure had become easy to follow and did not require significant effort. For Cara, however, almost none of the steps had been remembered as a regular and familiar pattern.

Other students in the classroom developed an understanding of patterns in learning, such as the natural and familiar task of using a textbook, opening to the correct page, and visually attending to the details of the text. Certain textbooks were located in specific cabinets in the classroom. Specific procedures were required in order to access these textbooks. For Cara, however, each time she was required to get a book for class, it was a new learning experience.

When she would begin to move to obtain her book, she became overwhelmed by the rush of other students, the colors of their clothing, the sounds, and the textures. Cara was having difficulty remembering the book procedure that had already been established in the rote memory of her classroom peers. Once she had her book, she had expended considerable energy and was too overwhelmed to participate in the lesson. Prior to the teacher beginning to teach the lesson from the textbook, Cara had already checked out. Forcing her to participate almost always resulted in a meltdown.

With the high potential for distractions and her need to intensely focus on the established classroom procedures, Cara frequently made errors. She was corrected and re-corrected by the teacher and other adults in the classroom. These adult-driven corrections further added to her confusion and her stress level. As it is with all of us, an increase in stress leads to diminished performance. In Cara's case, this would trigger wild behavior.

A program was initiated for Cara to help calm her within the classroom environment and to promote sustained learning-readiness behaviors. The primary focus was on Cara within the classroom setting, though many of the strategies would work at home as well. Something needed to be established to help Cara be calmer and more focused.

As a school-based occupational therapist*, I was enthusiastic to assist the team. I first observed Cara in her classroom and focused on understanding the role that Cara's sensory system played on calming her and in promoting emotional security. Good sensory integration* is the primary contributor to a child's sense of security and emotional control, something Cara sorely lacked. What she did to calm herself, I incorporated in her OT exercises.

The vestibular system,* and its connection to the rest of the sensory system, provides us with one of the most basic forms of physical and emotional security. It is also in charge of our sense of balance. It helps us move well. For these reasons, stimulation of the vestibular system became an integral part of Cara's OT routine. Cara needed breaks from her class work to promote calmness through vestibular activities, and other sensory exercises were initiated with the goal in mind of calmness, coherence and learning readiness. The specific exercises were designed by Cara without her realizing it.

During my classroom observation time while in the non-judgmental detective mode, I noted that Cara enjoyed challenging

* See Glossary for definition

her sense of balance and she enjoyed movement, all kinds of movement. She was observed to seek a great variety of different postures, including lying down on her back or tummy, crawling, and rolling. This told me that her brain needed these movements to stimulate her sensory system. These movements appeared to be necessary to assist Cara in maintaining her brain focus for full participation in a long school day. To that end, movement breaks* were pre-designated and scheduled frequently throughout the day.

During these scheduled break times, Cara and a classroom instructional aide would leave the classroom and walk out of doors to a different classroom location to perform crawling and jumping activities. Therapy balls* and other rolling devices were made available for Cara in this separate space. Cara also benefited from being outside in the fresh air where she would walk along the sidewalk or on the track.

Transitioning from outside of the classroom back into the structure of the classroom required specific instructions and lots of practice. The fine art of returning to the classroom was an exceptionally difficult task for Cara. It became necessary to practice quietly entering the classroom and sitting at her desk when the classroom was empty before she could do it with a room full of students.

The OT program also needed to help Cara with her poor sense of her own body boundaries. She lacked the foundational understanding regarding how much space her body took up. Navigating through a crowded classroom was an ordeal! Not knowing her body boundaries, she didn't understand what did and did not belong to her. She picked up everything in her path. She even ate food off other students' cafeteria trays when she walked past their table. Not cool!

To assist Cara in experiencing her body as separate from the environment, she needed to know how much space she occupied. Facilitating the recognition of her physical body boundaries began with compression exercises of the arms, legs and body, as well as head hugs. Compression exercises are outlined in the "Strategies to Try" section at the end of this chapter.

Using these compression exercises, Cara's height, length, and width were emphasized, which helped Cara experience where she started and ended. Continually knowing and re-asserting one's body boundaries is very calming for the brain. At the beginning of the day, the classroom aide would have Cara stand and perform head, shoulder, and extremity compression exercises to provide a calming start to the day. In addition, movement songs such as "head, shoulders, knees, and toes" as well as games such as "Simon says" and even an age-appropriate and classroom friendly game of "peek-a-boo" and "hide and go seek" were all activities that promoted a sense of self for Cara. Full class activities with partners, such as tracing their partner's full-body outline on huge sheets of paper, were repeated at intervals over the school year.

Following Cara's morning compression exercise, the next priority was helping her to understand the space around her. Knowing how to move and how to occupy space is a rudimentary skill necessary for students to function in the classroom. The teacher introduced concepts such as in, over, beside, and under in playing games such as zoo animals strutting in their cage, or circus animals parading. During one full class session, the classroom teacher and specialty trained adaptive physical education teacher* had the students pretend that they were lions wandering around the desks. The teacher encouraged under, through, beside, and over, which helped Cara develop an intimate and personal understanding of spatial awareness. An obstacle course was also very helpful in learning spatial awareness firsthand. Believe it or not, navigating through an obstacle course standing or crawling,

* See Glossary for definition

inside or outside the classroom, can be helpful in promoting positive learning behaviors while seated and doing deskwork.

Cara had one more OT problem for me to consider: everything went into her mouth! Perhaps because of an immature tactile system*, Cara was still relying on oral-motor* input in order to understand her world. Edible and non-edible objects, including her fingers, were placed in her mouth on a frequent basis. This behavior provided an ongoing indication to the school staff that Cara's tactile system was not functioning properly.

Until Cara could develop a heightened sense of tactile input through her fingertips, she would continue to rely on excessive oral input by mouthing everything. The OT goal for Cara was to improve her sense of touch through her fingertips and then gradually reduce her reliance on oral facilitation for understanding her world and, therefore, for calming herself.

Developmentally speaking, infants begin exploring their world by putting everything in their mouth. As their hand function progresses, they learn to explore the world with their fingers. The weight-bearing through the hands when crawling allows the motor cortex* a heightened appreciation of the hand. The pressure on the hands helps develop the brain-to-hand connection.

The school records indicated that Cara had never crawled as a young child. The OT program aimed to reproduce this important developmental stage with fun crawling games and with hand and arm compression exercises. Placing pressure through the fingertips was an attempt to reproduce the naturally occurring developmental stage so that her fingers' sense of touch could improve. The tactile program quickly helped Cara to decrease her reliance on the mouth and to increase reliance on information coming through her fingertips. The program that helped Cara shift from her mouth to exploring through her hands is outlined in the "Strategies to Try" section at the end of this chapter.

With this tactile program underway, the teacher could now appropriately discourage Cara from placing any objects or her fingers in her mouth during class time. As stated earlier, the transition from one developmental level to the next needs consideration. Cara's parents were asked to help. At home, they were instructed to remove Cara's fingers from her mouth and were told to gently place pressure through her fingers and hands. Eventually through the training using hand-over-hand assistance, Cara learned to squeeze her own hands. Classroom aides were able to remind Cara to do these compression exercises on her own hands. These strategies helped improve Cara's tactile sensitivity. She was also provided with a clear pencil* topper, which was seen to be an age-appropriate "chewy*" for Cara to gnaw on. Cara was encouraged to bring stimulating snacks for recess that facilitated oral chewing, such as carrots and fruit roll-ups, and she was permitted to chew gum when taking tests. Over time, Cara could perform more school activities with her hands away from her mouth.

In OT, we understand that many people use personal intervention strategies such as taking a deep breath or closing their eyes and counting backwards from ten to modulate the brain's ability to focus. Similar personal strategies needed to be developed for David, Logan and Cara as they did not naturally have the skill to modulate their own behavior. For each student, different kinds of activities were seen to help them diminish poor behavior and show improvement in learning-readiness skills.

Despite the differences between David, Logan and Cara, they also had similarities. Each of these students could function at a higher level when placed in an ideal environment with ideal circumstances. Each of these students' teachers learned to identify the circumstances that best promoted focused attention. These highly skilled teachers were also able to identify the circumstances that tended to trigger poor behavior. With the help of OT strategies, each teacher also became adept at assisting their students to modulate their responses in order to maintain a calmer and more coherent approach to school tasks.

David became more comfortable within the second-grade classroom environment. As the feeling of comfort increased, the frequency and the intensity of problematic behaviors diminished. He could more readily communicate his ideas and better focus on the skills and abilities of a second-grade student. David had an increased awareness of the importance of being understood through verbal and written language. He was highly internally motivated to produce a high standard of work for his classroom teacher. Over the course of the school year, David became more adept at exhibiting his knowledge within the safe environment of his familiar classrooms and peers. His sense of comfort and familiarity appeared to be directly linked to his successful performance. When he needed to take a break, his teacher created a circumstance for him to calm down. Elopement diminished and his peers continued to enjoy his company.

By the end of the high school year, Logan demonstrated improvement in his task completion behaviors*. In addition, the basics of right brain/left brain learning exercises and eye/hand coordination activities resulted in the surprising improved ability to form letters and words accurately and legibly. In the past, the effort required to concentrate long enough to provide accurate answers expended most of Logan's energy. This perceived laziness was the original and primary concern of Logan's parents. His parents had frequently complained to the school that the teachers had not emphasized teaching their son correct writing skills. At that time, Logan's parents didn't understand the VPT* mechanism that must be in place for fine motor* coordination to be successful. Now Logan's parents are very pleased with his printing and writing. David made up for the lack of VPT processing by consciously pressing his writing arm by his side to stabilize it and to lean into the leading edge of his desk to ensure a stable trunk (core) posture. He was developing his own personal strategies to compensate for any deficiencies in his VPT sensory processing system*. (More on fine motor coordination and legible printing in chapter 6.)

Understanding the effects of compromised VPT systems helped the adults in Cara's life to see patterns and make sense of her behavior. The astute school staff and her compassionate family members soon recognized that Cara needed more time than her peers in responding to a direction. When allowed this response time and not overly hurried, Cara was more successful at her school work and chores at home. As the classroom personnel better understood Cara's pace of doing, she was gradually more able to engage her mind in purposeful activity. Her response to the world became more understandable and easier to anticipate. With less stress impacting Cara and those around her, her mood began to even out.

The strategies identified throughout this chapter involve methods to stimulate the VPT sensory systems in order to calm the mind and body, leading to mental coherence. These methods are not only designed for individuals on the autism spectrum. When the mind and body function harmoniously, the results can be far reaching. In the next chapter, strategies are employed to assist students with difficulty moving their bodies in a smooth and coordinated manner. The VPT systems are, once again, identified as the primary common denominator in these children's gross motor* coordination challenges. Before you go to the next chapter, consider the following section on strategies and immediate solutions for the unique learner on the autism spectrum.

* See Glossary for definition

STRATEGIES TO TRY

IF your child or student unique learner is acting irrationally,

THEN observe your child like a detective would and see if there are patterns to her or his actions. Some things may seem to trigger negative behaviors and other things seem to trigger positive, calm and coherent behaviors. Don't be surprised to discover that your child's odd behavior is actually your child attempting to calm themselves. Some unique learners on the autism spectrum need to flap their hands or spin their body to calm themselves. Best advice: try not to assume that it is always due to bad behavior.

IF your child or student appears to move a lot, either physically moving from their seat to roam around the room, tapping feet or pencils, wiggling, shifting, or other continuous movement (this indicates that the child's brain needs their body to move in order to stay alert),

THEN provide a fidget for the child. Fidgets* are any small device, like a toy or resistive putty, that provides stimulation through the tactile sense and is enjoyed by the student. The fidget acts as a substitute for the continuous need to move.

IF your child or student has become too wound up and is

unable to get back to the task at hand,

THEN study your child's behavior and set pre-designated break times. For example, if your child can attend to an activity at home or in the classroom for 30-40 minutes before a meltdown, set a pre-designated break roughly every 30 minutes. Your child may need to move to a special and safe environment where they can run around. Some children need to run, walk, swing, somersault, or roll in order to better engage their vestibular system. Others may need heavy resistance to activate their proprioceptive system*. Examples of heavy resistance include performing heavy jobs such as carrying a jug of milk or a heavy container. In addition, kicking over stacked objects such as shoe boxes or empty tennis ball containers also activates the sensory system and can help a child who needs movement and the feeling of resistance in order to wake up their brain.

IF your child or student becomes irritated or distracted by excessive noise,

THEN provide him or her with noise cancellation headphones.

IF your child or student is more mature and capable of understanding that they are responsible for their own shifts in mood,

THEN they need your help to better plan and anticipate the activities in their day. They need to understand how to wait it out* when frustrations and anger overwhelm them.

* See Glossary for definition

By waiting it out, they can avoid the cascade of (angry) chemical release that surges throughout the brain and body.

IF your child or student seems to get stuck in their thinking or their doing and can't seem to get over it and move on,

THEN exercises to work the right and left sides of the brain and the body can be helpful. These right brain/left brain processing skills are also used by athletes to promote heightened performance. Examples of right brain/left brain learning exercises are as follows:

Crossing the midline—The midline is an imaginary line that vertically divides the body into two halves. Because the right side of the brain controls the left side of the body and vice versa, crossing the midline can stimulate the two hemispheres of the brain to function together. An example of crossing the midline is when the left hand reaches across (the midline) to the right side of the body to pick something up. Tasks to promote crossing the midline are very important to promote whole brain development. Card games intentionally set up to cross the midline, such as memory or solitaire, and basic card tricks all emphasize planning as well as crossing the midline. Tossing a ball or a beanbag from one hand to the other (think juggling) is also beneficial. Yoga, dance, swimming, soccer and martial arts employ complex crossing of the body's midline by using large body movements. Even the game of pickup sticks is highly beneficial, especially when accompanied with verbal reasoning skills prior to turn taking.

Visual-motor tracking*—Visual-motor tracking is how a person's eyes move in synchrony together to follow a moving object or a line of text. One should try to only move the eyes while keeping the head still. Require the student to draw a circle around each letter of the alphabet in correct sequence within a nonsense paragraph made up of imaginary words. These nonsense paragraphs should encompass all the letters of the alphabet from A-Z. Begin by timing the student (or having them time themselves depending on the student's age and ability), aiming toward a 60-second timeframe. Bouncing and catching a ball also incorporates visual-motor tracking awareness as well as sports incorporating balls (basketball, baseball, tennis).

Spatial awareness—Spatial awareness* is the ability to organize visual information and understand how it is changed as it rotates and moves through space. Multiple squiggles of lines on a page can challenge spatial awareness. Students are asked to visually track from the start point to the end of the jumbled lines in a consistent manner. First require the student to track with his or her finger, then with a pencil, and then visually only. As the student progresses, attach the worksheet to a wall and have the student do the exercise while in various postures: standing, standing on one foot, and standing on one foot with one hand placed over the opposite eye. Folding a paper airplane or other basic origami activities also provides an exercise in spatial awareness. Older or more able students can be required to verbally relay their plans prior to initiating the folding project to add a mental planning component to this task.

———

IF your child or student seems to think everything belongs to them, they grab and possess everything in their path, and

* See Glossary for definition

they may even walk right into furniture or other children,

THEN they need to learn the parameters of their own body so they can sort out what is self and what is not self. This process of individuating* themselves from the world that surrounds them needs your help. Try compression exercises. Compression exercises are performed on the arms and legs, and even the head, by using both of your hands to squeeze your child's extremity along its entire length. This squeeze is about the same pressure that you might use to gently squeeze the water from a large sponge with both hands. The head hugs are performed by placing a hand on either side of the head and applying a gentle compression. (Compression exercises take about two minutes total to perform on the head, arms and legs.)

IF your child or student is constantly putting fingers and non-edible items in their mouth and they are beyond infancy, they are demonstrating a deficiency in their tactile system,

THEN your child needs help shifting their brain's over-reliance on their mouth. They need to explore their world with their hands and fingers, not their lips and tongue. Pressure on the hands and fingers helps to develop the communication between the brain and the hand and improve the awareness of touch. Activities such as crawling, tossing and catching a weighted ball or beanbag, as well as modified pushups, all apply pressure to the hand and help to awaken touch receptors. Specifically, stimulating the sense of touch by allowing your child to move their hands through a sensory bin, such as a shoebox-sized container that has been filled with different textures and materials,* helps to refine touch and promote a more mature discriminative sense of touch necessary to hold a pencil. Try using materials in the shoebox such as rice, dried beans, or small patches of cloth, to provide variety and to develop their sense of touch. Vary the activity by having them find items like marbles and small toys within the materials. Change the material in the sensory bin frequently. Also try macaroni, cotton balls, flour, or sand.

During this stage, it is also important to allow some limited oral-motor (mouth) exercises such as encouraging snacking on hard foods such as carrots, celery, and dried fruit. Nontoxic children's chew devices (a "chewy"*) are also available commercially. Until the child can fully switch to their fingertips for exploration, they will need some oral-motor activities.

* See Glossary for definition

CHAPTER FIVE

THE REAL ISSUE: DEALING WITH GROSS MOTOR PROBLEMS

Claire had a huge bandage covering her knee when she came into the clinic with her parents for her first OT* appointment. She had bandages on her elbows and red scrapes on the palms of her hands from a fall she had taken at school. Claire sank down in her chair as her mother described how Claire had fallen during recess that day: "She simply fell down the stairs for no reason." Claire's parents described their daughter frequently sliding into furniture, bumping into family members, and poorly negotiating the location of the pet dog while stumbling over his tail. At times, Claire would bump into the wooden door frame of her bedroom, seemingly forgetting the location of the door frame as well as the exact anatomical parameters of her own 10-year-old body. Today, she even fell on the school stairway.

Apart from the bandages, Claire looked like any other child, a little tall for her 10 years of age with a lovely and attentive face. She was wearing brightly colored clothing with matching ribbons that held her light brown ponytail in place. But the bandages were an ongoing testament to her coordination problems. The doctor had told Claire's parents that she was healthy and normal in terms of her physical development. Her clumsiness was explained as "going through a growth spurt."

Another student with coordination problems, Adam, was referred to OT by his fifth grade teacher. The teacher said Adam looked exhausted all the time. He expressed concern regarding Adam's difficulty with math lessons and Adam's tendency to not complete worksheets. Claire, in the fourth grade, was thought to be clumsy. Adam, in the fifth grade, was thought to be lazy. Both students were similar in that their muscles just couldn't keep up with the commands of their brain. Both students had been told time and time again to try harder.

Claire's mother relayed that Claire had had difficulty following through with their request for her to clear the dinner table while at home the previous night. She seemed to need repetition of each step of the task. She couldn't recall the overall instructions despite being 10 years of age and having cleared the table many, many times. Claire's mother also described her difficulties in following through with tasks at school. Academic tasks, family games, and any sport activity seemed to escape Claire's understanding and her ability to fully participate.

When I observed Adam in his math class, he worked at a pace slower than his peers. He appeared to be trying as hard as he could even though he had copied only the first two sentences from the front board while his classmates had moved ahead and were copying and solving sentence number five of the six total problems. His teacher thought that Adam didn't follow instructions properly. The teacher wondered if Adam wasn't listening. He wondered if Adam didn't understand the importance of school as he was always fooling around. He saw Adam turned around in his seat or slumped over his desk or leaning so far back that he looked half asleep.

Claire's parents sought out OT at her teacher's recommendation. They obtained a doctor referral for OT in order to improve gross motor* coordination and independence in daily living skills (dressing, feeding, personal hygiene). During her first visit, Claire's ability to plan and execute movement was assessed. As in most OT assessments that I perform, I was looking for Claire's life skill strengths and areas of weakness as well as her ability to communicate and to problem solve.

The assessment revealed that, in terms of her balance and co-ordination, Claire had significant difficulty navigating a simple obstacle course that I had set up in the OT clinic. She had difficulty standing on one foot for more than three or four seconds with her eyes open and was incapable of balancing on either foot with eyes closed. She was unable to reproduce or mimic familiar postures frequently used by occupational therapists* to assess strength and coordination of postural muscles.

Claire had difficulty following simple verbal instructions such as "Lie down with your head at this end." When asked to sit, Claire tended to sit in a collapsed and rounded forward posture. Her standing posture was maintained with an extreme arch, like a gymnast in a dismount position. She also tended to walk with a wider base of support and her feet rotated outward. Running was clearly a non-preferred activity and done for a brief moment only. After much coaxing on my part, I could see why running was no fun. Her feet landed on the ground in a very heavy and slap-down manner. It was hard for her to run a straight line and the whole motion looked uncomfortable for her knees and her back.

All these difficulties Claire had with poor coordination very clearly affected her ability to function at home and at school. She lacked strength and stability of the postural support muscles* that should hold her trunk stable. She had poor control of the dynamic moving muscles* that swing the arms and legs. She had poor control of her posture in general.

In OT, we recognize that problems such as poor coordination or clumsiness are really problems with a child's ability feel gravity and respond with the correct muscles. Balancing and moving require muscle strength and fluidity to correctly respond to the effects of gravity.

It quickly became clear to Claire's parents that clumsiness was just one symptom of Claire's challenges. The difficulties in Claire's VPT sensory systems* contributed to her appearance of clumsiness. The problems with her sensory processing* created huge gaps in her ability to relate to her peers and to enjoy meaningful relationships. These deficits also limited her ability to participate fully in her academic curriculum. Claire's mother worried about her daughter's self-esteem. Claire's sad comment "I just don't fit in" was unfortunately very true.

At school, Claire had covered up her troubled performance with more than the bandages I saw in my office. She had developed a way to disguise her learning problems. She had her own personal coping strategies to prevent others from discovering her inability to complete fourth-grade school work, without really knowing it was a strategy. Claire would create diversions and distractions so that she would not have to follow the established rules or the specific directions. In fact, she changed the rules of most games she played. She even moved home base.

At the age of 10, Claire would take charge and control her friends' recess activities. The rules of her games and the goals of her activities would change at a dizzying pace to mask her inability to follow the regular rules. Peers had difficulty following Claire's logic and would eventually disengage. By the end of recess, Claire would either beg forgiveness or demonstrate impatience and irritation toward her friends.

Usually by the end of the 15-minute recess period, Claire had exhausted herself attempting to sustain the attention of her peers during recess play activities. It seemed that no one wanted to be friends with this type of classmate for very long. Even Claire's mother noticed that Claire had difficulty sustaining friendships due to Claire's insistence on being in charge of the rules of the game.

Claire oscillated between expressing frustration toward her peers and expressing frustration toward herself. Claire experienced hurt feelings and made self-deprecating remarks exaggerating her condition. Despite what adults sometimes told her, Claire was well aware that she was already trying very hard! Recently, she had begun describing herself as being stupid. By the time the school day ended, Claire was exhausted by the strain of getting through another day in the life of a fourth-grade student.

Adam attended a different school from Claire, but in the same community. I met him when he was in fifth grade. An academic-related OT evaluation was recommended for suggestions to improve coordination. Adam's postural support muscles didn't allow him to sit upright for very long. As a result, most of the class time was spent slouching. Slouching posture caused difficulty coordinating his hand for smooth writing. His written work was done very slowly and looked very untidy. His gross motor coordination problems were making it hard for him to succeed in school.

Over the previous three to four years, Adam's parents responded to the problem by doing much of Adam's schoolwork for him. His well-meaning parents did not like to see Adam frustrated. They knew their son was intelligent and hardworking and they just thought he needed to grow up and get stronger. Adam's parents hadn't realized how much of Adam's work they were really doing for him. They hadn't stopped to consider that each year they seemed to take on more and more of their son's school responsibilities.

Although a variety of OT assessments were performed, testing Adam for his postural strength was very important to me. It provided information regarding his muscles and joints, his balance, and his coordination of overall movement. Sitting up requires more than just strong muscles, and sitting up correctly is required for efficient printing and typing. Notice how your posture can change the function of your arm and hand in the following example:

To get a sense of Adam's posture and to help you become aware of your own postural habits, try sitting as Adam does. Without strong core muscles Adam sits with a very rounded back. To experience this, place your feet flat on the floor and let your trunk collapse forward in a slouched sitting posture. Feel your shoulders round forward and note how that causes the neck and head to assume a downward-looking posture. Now, imagine you are a student and must look up at the front of the class. In your slouched posture (stay collapsed forward), try to look upward. Feel your chin thrust forward. In this same chin-thrust forward posture, try turning your head and rotating it from side to side. Notice that your neck doesn't move very much while in this posture. Notice how tiring it is to look up and around, in front, and beside you. Notice how effortful it is to raise your arm.

Try it again, but tuck your chin in and sit up straight. Notice that it is much easier to turn the head and neck and to use your visual system when in a good posture. Raising your hand in response to a teacher's question is much easier when you sit upright. This is because correct posture not only improves the alertness and the function of the sensory processing system* (your eyes and ears), but it also promotes a learning-ready brain.

In terms of postural support, Adam had difficulty lifting a 7-pound barbell. His brain wasn't able to sort out all of the associated muscles' functions. The muscles were strong, but the sensory messages to the muscles were disrupted. Lifting a 7-pound

* See Glossary for definition

barbell is a different quality of muscle work than lifting a lighter object, such as an ice cream cone. The VPT sensory system provides the background ability to lift heavy gym weights as compared to lifting an ice cream cone toward your mouth.

Adam's muscles were healthy, but the system to tell the muscle what to do and when to do it was compromised. As a result, the muscles lacked the appearance of strength and efficiency. This had been going on for Adam for a very long time! Inefficient muscles led to poor coordination of his finger muscles for printing. His elbow was either too stiff or too loose.

The elbow muscles depend on other muscles to stabilize the shoulder and the shoulder blade before it can bend the elbow. In addition to muscles providing strength, they must also work in concert with the rest of the body. The relationship of the shoulder blade to the rib cage, and the rib cage to the spine, is essential for the elbow to function correctly. The shoulder blade must be still against the rib cage in order for the elbow to work. The muscle that extends the elbow, the triceps muscle, must receive the command to be turned off so that the biceps muscle can bend the elbow without fighting against triceps. Muscle coordination is a very complex and multi-sensory achievement. It can impact how we reason and how we function at work and at school.

Claire's full evaluation involved a conversation with her school teacher. Having already seen Claire at our clinic, it was not surprising to discover that Claire had similar difficulties in the classroom. Her teacher and I spoke over the phone and she described the difficulties within the classroom. Problems were evident to Claire's teacher because of Claire's inability to follow through with tasks, her reduced sitting tolerance, and her frequent mishandling of tools and equipment.

Claire was described as unintentionally handling items too roughly and damaging equipment, such as pressing too hard while sharpening a pencil and repeatedly breaking pencil tips when printing. Levers and buttons would inadvertently break when it was Claire's turn to play with that item. Incorrect stepping and general poor coordination in the classroom frequently resulted in Claire bumping into student desks and interrupting other students' ability to write or draw. She distracted others from their school work when classmates attempted to assist her with broken pencils, stuck zippers, and lost equipment.

Puzzle pieces were put back in the box in a disorganized fashion so that the lid could not be closed despite Claire's overuse of her only strategy: repeatedly pushing the box lid down harder and harder. Until a classmate pointed it out, Claire did not appear to have the skill to see that the puzzle pieces needed to be reorganized and the box lid needed to be handled with better coordination versus Claire's forceful pushing on the box lid.

In the OT clinic, the evaluation demonstrated that Claire had a very poor understanding of her body. She had difficulty recognizing the size and space that her physical body occupied. Usually children achieve the developmental milestone of understanding their body's parameter through childhood games such as hide and go seek. A young child quickly discovers that they are too large to hide in a shoe box and better suited to hide in a closet. Typically developing children have a sense of their personal space reliably functioning by the time of kindergarten or first grade.

Claire had not yet established her understanding of left and right. She had difficulty with spatial awareness*, such as during a game when asked to stand above the blue dot located on the floor or to sit underneath the green table. Claire had not generalized spatial awareness concepts, such as above, below, beside, in front, and behind. In short, Claire's understanding of her body and her body in relationship to other objects in space, such as furniture in Claire's path, was significantly impaired.

　　　　　　　* See Glossary for definition

Young children practice spatial awareness through developmentally appropriate games that allow them to rehearse the concept of space, including the amount of space they take up. Dress-up allows children to see their physical size in relation to the adult clothing that they are using to play dress-up. A simple game of tag incorporates spatial awareness that can help a child learn how much space is needed between themselves and another participant in the game in order to avoid being caught or tagged. Claire's parents described Claire as stopping just short of her target family member when playing tag. "It's as if she thinks she has a huge arm span. Why doesn't she just run closer to me?" Or when playing soccer, "She runs right through the ball and doesn't stop to kick it at the right time."

These examples of spatial awareness challenges in Claire's three-dimensional world had profound overlap with difficulties showing up in the two-dimensional world of classroom academics. Reading and writing use two-dimensional symbols, also necessitating an understanding of spatial awareness.

Students must have an intimate understanding of spatial awareness concepts in order to appreciate the distinction between a lower-case letter b, p, and d. The vertical line and attached semi-circle has a profoundly different meaning when it is left-facing or right-facing. Additionally, the orientation of the semi-circle toward the top or the bottom of the vertical line is another cue in decoding the letter. All this decoding is made more complicated because the letters are written on a paper that has horizontal lines. Claire had difficulty decoding the letter symbols and organizing a mental map to appreciate space between words. Claire's lack of spatial awareness took the outward form of clumsiness, but that was a small part of the whole story.

Claire and Adam both had problems with their VPT systems. They both benefited greatly from PE and recess activities with their peers that incorporated gross motor games. The activities helped them develop important brain connections necessary for learning, such as left/right orientation and spatial awareness. Gross motor activities during PE and recess heightened their ability to participate in a classroom activity even while seated at a desk. Their bodies were learning at these PE and recess times. For both of these students, this kind of physical activity was seen to be crucial to their classroom success.

Feeling gravity through the vestibular system* and feeling movement through the proprioceptive system* inform the tactile system* to better organize the muscles for gross motor control leading to fine motor control. This means that gross motor skills must be addressed before fine motor skills* if both are deficient. (More about fine motor in chapter 6.)

Improved control allows for correct and accurate movement. Stimulation of the VPT systems actually helps the brain in processing complex visual and auditory information. Better "look and listen" skills in the classroom are helped by gross motor fun at recess and PE time. VPT stimulation, inevitable during recess and PE activities, leads to better fine motor control for school work involving pencils and scissors.

Both Claire and Adam were included in developing their own VPT sensory home and school exercises. They were taught how the VPT systems were necessary to function adequately before the looking and listening abilities could work properly. Looking and listening are relied upon in all school classes and especially necessary during seated desk tasks. Therefore, the VPT portion of the sensory system was augmented at home because the visual and auditory portions of the sensory system were already being exercised while at school.

Claire had to learn that her eyes and ears could work for learning and for making friends much better when her body could learn to move smoothly and comfortably. It was explained to her that her teachers could help her develop her eyes and ears for success in learning through looking and listening, but it would be up to Claire to work on developing her VPT systems.

Claire's "good ideas" list involved activities that many adults would view as roughhousing, but Claire's parents developed an understanding of the need for Claire to alter her position with gravity to stimulate her vestibular system. She was permitted to somersault in the living room, perform a headstand safely against a designated wall with a large pillow underneath her head and upper body, as well as an enjoyable home exercise involving rolling down a small hill in their backyard. Claire and her mother purchased a beginner yoga program that they could watch together on their TV. Performing the various postures truly challenged them both and helped improve their understanding of the body and the body's response to a change in the center of gravity.

Swimming, dancing, and bike riding were incorporated as a regular weekly movement diet. Trips to the local playground to enjoy the playground equipment became a valid home activity leading toward heightened school successes. Activities incorporating a great range and variety of postures and movement stimulated her VPT system. Claire's favorite activity was swinging and her parents were able to attach a tire swing to their large backyard tree where Claire could swing, spin, and climb.

When Claire and her parents better understood the role of touch and tactile processing to assist the brain for learning, a huge range of home activities were quickly identified. Every day Claire tried to teach her skin new feelings. Clothing items were selected for variety in textures. Claire had a plethora of toothbrushes, hairbrushes, and combs to expose herself to different textures for brushing her teeth or brushing her hair. She had a variety of scrub brushes and loofah sponges to enjoy new textures introduced to her skin during bath and shower time.

We developed a 3-point rating scale for textures and tactile items (1, 2, and 3: nice, ok, and not nice). For example, the use of a scrub brush on the sole of her feet was rated "3, not nice." Claire practiced scrubbing with a face cloth, then a loofah sponge, and gradually the soles of her feet could tolerate a scrub brush. This 3-point scale of "nice, ok, not nice" was used for a great variety of clothing items and activities. She used a variety of different textured pens and pencils. Her favorite was a velvet-coated pencil. She even explored different textures of pillows to sit upon while having her dinner or doing her homework. All of these ideas were generated by Claire and supported by her parents.

While at school, Claire discovered that certain desk exercises helped her brain stay alert. She had three favorite exercises to keep focused. The first was making gentle and repetitive fists, three times. The second was pushing the palms of her hands together at her midline* (picture "praying" hands). The third was a seated press-up that she also enjoyed. It was done at her desk by placing the palms of her hands on the seat of her school chair and then straightening her elbows to lift her body slightly off the seat pan surface. These "good ideas" served to wake up Claire's brain for learning. She would do three repetitions of each, at the very beginning of every class.

While Adam was at school, he needed improved awareness of his postural support muscles. Adam was provided with a wedge-shaped seat cushion that was 2 inches in height at the back and only a ½ inch in height at the front. When sitting, Adam benefited from this dense foam-wedge cushion to position his low back correctly. It improved his posture and the stability of his back muscles. He found it easier to hold his head upright when using the wedge cushion.

Adam also needed exercises to stimulate static* and dynamic muscle control* and he needed better balance. He needed to feel gravity, an experience registered in the vestibular sensory

* See Glossary for definition

system, in all kinds of ways, such as when riding a bike, using a swing, running, jumping, balancing on a low balance beam, skateboarding, and snow skiing.

Adam was encouraged to sit on a dynamic and unstable surface such as a therapy ball*. The large therapy ball became a "round chair" and was used as Adam's seated surface. He had to sit in correct posture or he would feel himself sliding down the ball. Constantly correcting his balance and keeping the ball still by sitting upright was very challenging at first, but Adam progressed from a 5-minute tolerance up to 25 minutes in just a one-month period of time. Adam's muscle tone improved. His teacher no longer complained of his "lazy" posture.

Muscles work together. Some muscles are biased to gently and statically contract to provide strength, stability and to hold the body still, while other muscles dynamically contract and provide motion to the arms and legs, neck and trunk. The coordination of the static and dynamic muscles is referred to as muscle tone.

Both Claire and Adam needed exercises to increase trunk strength, muscle tone and coordination. Two exercises we worked on were cocoons and airplanes. The exercise called cocoons is performed by lying on your back. Cocoons strengthen the tummy muscles. Airplanes are performed by lying on your tummy and they strengthen the back muscles.

A successful cocoon suggests the student's coordination of their movement system is intact for these postural muscles. The ability to perform an airplane is directly linked to good sitting posture. Both exercises are very beneficial for students with coordination problems. A description of these exercises is provided in the "Strategies to Try" section at the end of this chapter.

Both Claire and Adam were encouraged to participate in activities that facilitated an improved understanding of spatial awareness. Strategies, exercises and activities to promote spatial awareness are outlined in the "Strategies to Try" section at the end of this chapter.

During clinic-based OT sessions, Claire was exposed to a variety of movement experiences to stimulate her sensory system. Incorporated in these multisensory* sessions was an emphasis on vestibular (balance), proprioceptive (movement) and tactile stimulation. The movement exercises are outlined in the "Strategies to Try" section at the end of this chapter.

Slower timing and rhythm were encouraged when possible for doing tasks at home and during family games and activities. Her parents helped Claire smooth out her erratic pace of doing. They no longer praised her for the speed of her performance and, instead, encouraged a consistent rate and pace.

Claire's parents noticed that Claire seemed to function best when she was encouraged to slow down. They recognized that a slower pace of doing would become an important life skill for their daughter. They also helped Claire to champion a more consistent and middle-of-the-road approach to life. Of course, ups and downs, highs and lows, celebration and support were present in Claire's family as they are in most families, but they no longer rewarded Claire's tendency to believe that she was "master of the universe." The problem with this belief was that Claire also believed in the flip side, the opposite of self-confidence: a sense of "complete failure."

It is important for all of us to realize that the very challenges that tend to create difficulties for students like Claire and Adam at school can frequently become the very source of their success when they mature. Adam became an adept swimming competitor and practiced martial arts on a regular basis. These movement experiences helped integrate his sensory system, reduce stress and maintain a sense of well-being.

With a better understanding of her students' behaviors, Claire's teacher began to incorporate multisensory learning*. This skilled educator was now aware that many activities and games that may look like her students are merely playing, actually work many facets of the brain needed for learning. The right kind of fun can lead to adeptness in class work.

Children tend to enjoy games that stimulate their brains. They find great amusement in toys that tap into the exact developmental level that their brain should be working at in order to naturally mature. Infants giggle and small children find fascination in games that point their minds toward the next developmental level. Through this process, Claire's parents and teachers came to recognize that children truly have a developmental need to learn.

Many unique learners need to refocus their entire brain and sensory system in order to become receptive to learning. In the next chapter, a multisensory learning approach is directed toward reducing the problem of messy printing. For most of us, printing seems to be something that happens only at the fingers. However, printing is actually the endpoint of a highly evolved and mature sensory-motor system*. Maturation of the whole body helps make printing possible and it is the whole body that must be incorporated to correct printing problems. But first, consider the following "Strategies to Try" section on immediate solutions for reduced gross motor coordination.

STRATEGIES TO TRY

IF your child or student has poor posture with a slumped forward appearance, they may have weak trunk muscles that can cause fatigue when trying to look forward to the front of the classroom,

THEN the child needs to improve their trunk (or core) muscle strength. Trunk strengthening exercises are helpful, such as cocoons and airplanes. Cocoons are performed by having the child lie on their back and asking them to bringing their knees up to the chest and hugging the knees with their arms tightly. Have them raise their head so their nose is going toward their knees. Try to hold this position for a count of 10. Repeat 10 times.

An airplane is performed by lying on the tummy and raising the legs, arms, and head up off the floor. This airplane position, with head lifted above the floor, involves neck muscles that are necessary for good head control and for good visual control. Hold for a count of 10. Repeat 10 times.

In addition, problems with seated posture can be corrected by having the student use a wedge-shaped seat cushion, such as a cushion that tends to be roughly two inches in height at the back and only half inch height in front. Sitting on this sloped surface positions the hips and the low back to allow a more upright and correct sitting posture. The student may need a footstool (or an inverted shoebox) if the cushion lifts them up so high that their feet no longer touch the floor.

IF your child or student seems to lose their balance, bump into things, collide with other people and is very inaccurate in their schoolwork,

THEN your child or student may struggle with spatial awareness and will benefit from vestibular exercises. Vestibular exercises to promote the understanding of spatial awareness (such as the correct direction for left, right, up, and down) and to promote correct navigating without bumping into obstacles are suggested below:

Summersaults, swinging, playing "matador" with a blanket that the child runs through like a (friendly) charging bull, crab walking (performed by sitting on the ground with knees bent and palms down, then the hips are raised off the floor and the child crawls in a tummy-facing-up position), standard crawling on all fours, playing catch, playing hopscotch, singing songs with rhythmic hand movements, playing marching band, dancing, or using a hula hoop.

Older children may enjoy the following vestibular activities:

Using a therapy ball as a seated surface, riding a bike, using a swing, running, jumping, balancing on a low balance beam, skateboarding, snow skiing, swimming, dancing, or practicing martial arts.

IF your unique learner student seems restless while in class,

THEN remember that unique learners benefit from PE and recess activities that incorporate gross motor strengthening for better posture and coordination. PE and recess should not be considered as a reward but as a usual and necessary part of the academic curriculum. When your child is at home, "Go outside and play" is still a very, very important part of your child's day.

IF your child or student seems consistently clumsy and uncoordinated,

THEN try proprioceptive activities at home and in small groups during PE to help them develop better coordination. Try any of the following exercises and modify them for your child's preferences and needs:

Create stepping stones from paper or cloth and practice jumping from stone to stone. Try this with one foot or two. (Be careful not to choose a material that may cause them to slip.)

Place a long rope on the floor and ask your child to keep one foot on one side and the other foot on the opposite side of the rope. Walk or run the length of the rope and vary this by making the rope have loops and turns.

Obtain a stretchy band material and tie this in a loop so that your child can attempt to move the stretchy loop from over their head and down their body, down to their feet, and to step out of the loop. Then try to do it from the feet up.

Use the same stretchy band material and ask the child to try to pull it apart so that their arms can feel the resistance increase as their arms are spread wider apart. Repeat this with a beanbag on the child's head to encourage good posture. This can be advanced by asking the child to stand on one foot only.

Use masking tape to tape shapes on the floor. Each shape could require a different physical movement. A square, for example, may require jumping up and down, a circle may require touching the floor, a triangle may require turning around once. Add rhythm and timing with music, a metronome, or clapping.

IF your child has trouble staying alert in the classroom,

THEN they need to stimulate their brain. Strategies for use while at school employing proprioceptive (pressure-like sensation) and tactile stimulation will help to keep a student's brain alert. Encourage the student to make gentle and repetitive fists so that they can feel the muscles in their hand squeezing. Pushing the palms of their hands together at their midline ("praying" hands) is also helpful as well as performing chair press-ups by placing the palms on the seat pan of the chair while straightening the elbows and lifting the body off the seat pan. Five repetitions of any of these strategies should be sufficient to wake up the brain for learning.

Stimulating the brain to improve alertness can be achieved through a home program for the tactile system. Although these strategies don't really lend themselves to use at school, encourage your child to try new feelings on their skin each day. Different clothing items, styles of toothbrushes, hairbrushes, and combs will introduce your child to different textures and feelings. Using a variety of scrub brushes and sponges in the shower or bath is also helpful. You can start with objects and textures that your child tolerates and then gradually introduce textures that are more difficult. The brain and the skin are closely connected. In the school I worked at, we taught students how to really wash and scrub their hands clean. We tell them, "Scrub your hands, scrub your brain (awake)!"

CHAPTER SIX

THE MESSY PRINTING SYNDROME: POOR FINE MOTOR SKILLS

There is always a loner on the school playground. They linger at the fringes watching the other students having fun, or they hang around the adult supervisor and pretend that they just aren't interested in playing. Micah was that student. He could be spotted on the school grounds secluded and alone, hanging off to the side of the activity. He stood on the perimeter of the tetherball court. He stood on the perimeter of the foursquare game enjoyed by his peers, and he held back when his friends and fellow students rushed out at recess to quickly collect the balls, hula-hoops, and jump ropes that these other students coveted.

When invited to play with the other children, Micah quickly became confused by the rules and the complex sequence of turn taking. He lacked the eye/hand coordination to successfully perform the physical action of the game. Micah had difficulty kicking a soccer ball accurately. He had difficulty timing the rhythm necessary to contact the tetherball at the exact moment necessary to execute an offensive attack on his opponent. If he was hit by the ball, he would exhibit an exaggerated response and discontinue the game, tearfully insinuating that his opponent had purposefully directed the ball to harm him.

Well-meaning adults would try to support Micah by suggesting he move a little farther from the ball to avoid crowding it. They would ask Micah's opponent to contact the ball softly. They would try coaching Micah, inviting him to watch closely, stand evenly, and swing hard. Though intended to be helpful, this was of little use for Micah, as he could not decipher what needed to occur with his joints and muscles to watch closely, stand evenly, or to swing hard. Micah was unable to decode these tips and cues in a meaningful way to alter his physical actions.

In response to the advice to not crowd the tetherball by moving farther away from it, Micah relocated his body at a significant distance to the tetherball pole and could not reach the ball at all. The adult had actually meant for Micah to hit the ball with his elbows extended to get a better purchase on the ball versus Micah's tendency to hold tightly bent arms and contact the ball too close to his body with poor leverage for an effective hit. Upon observing Micah's interpretation of the advice, the same adult was unable to alter the coaching tip and guide Micah further. They expressed profound surprise at his inability to follow the initial simple directions and encouragement.

In fact, Micah's action of stepping away from the tether ball, rendering him too far to even contact or play with the ball, was misinterpreted to mean that Micah was just not trying. It seemed Micah was mocking the adult by over-exaggerating the advice. Naturally, the adult quit. The adult, in this case, had his or her own personal life experiences and emotional bumps and bruises. From this perspective then, quite naturally, the adult felt hurt that Micah did not accept the advice. Micah was assumed disingenuous and ungrateful. Micah held a blank look on his face. He was confused. He stepped back and removed himself from the game.

He stood with his rounded shoulders and with his eyes looking far off at no particular target. The buzz of the recess bell ended the "fun" play. The end of recess came as a great relief to Micah. In this recess activity, of course, Micah did not have fun. He experienced a highly stressful and confusing 15 minutes outdoors in the sunshine. His break from the rigorous demands of his fourth-grade curriculum was spent emotionally navigating around his peers and adults on the playground.

For Micah, the classroom environment was usually far less anxiety provoking than the complexities of surviving recess during the unstructured playground time*. However, his class work on this day was negatively impacted by his recess tetherball trauma. Micah, and those around him, all saw a different Micah. The adult at recess saw a mocking child. The students saw an incapable classmate holding up the tetherball line. Micah saw himself as a misfit and felt other students were staring at him. Everyone was operating from his or her own perspective.

Perhaps you are of the perspective that this child really should just try harder. Maybe Micah's story reminds you of yourself and of obstacles you overcame by trying harder. This recess story might remind you of your child and the impossible patience required to teach him a new chore. With time and practice, many things can be overcome and much can be learned. Micah and children like him, however, require a different perspective. Try this difference in perspectives between yourself, the driver, and your passenger:

Imagine yourself on a road upon which you have never traveled. In addition to being curvy and mountainous, the road is in ill repair and traffic is heavy. Four lanes of cars zip along in a space that should only fill three lanes. You aren't sure where you need to turn next and are relying solely on your GPS system to navigate.

You are driving a large rental truck and towing an empty trailer. You have never driven this type of truck nor towed a trailer before. As a result, the size and smooth operation of your vehicle are a mystery. Perhaps you have a passenger who provides you with driving tips, "Don't cross the line!" and "Be more careful. Don't let the trailer drift into the other lane on the curves." These are all well-meaning suggestions but hard to execute because of the unknown parameters of the large vehicle and trailer. The disconnect between yourself and the vehicle is profound. "Where does the trailer begin and end?" you wonder to yourself.

If you can actually imagine how insecure and confused you would feel in this scenario, then you are beginning to understand how Micah feels. Many children experience this kind of disconnect in their bodies every single day of their lives. Micah's poor coordination in class and on the playground related to his profound disconnect between his brain (the driver) and his body (the vehicle).

Despite all of these challenges with Micah's coordination on the playground, what Micah's teacher was concerned about was his poor fine motor skills* in the classroom. She noticed that he worked hard, but his printing was very immature. Micah labored away at his rudimentary printing skills. Though he was a fourth-grade student, he had tremendous difficulty printing legibly and at the age-appropriate level for neatness and speed of performance. Micah felt that his writing looked like a first-grader's. Sometimes, even Micah could not read his own writing. When he couldn't decipher his own homework list, he was too embarrassed to ask for help.

Sloppy printing can easily be construed as lazy or careless behavior; however, this is a clue that the detective observer* in you should now be able to recognize as a symptom of a larger problem. If you have a unique learner in your life, you already know that no fourth-grade student wants their printing to look like a first-grader wrote it! It is safe to assume that your unique learner has, like Micah, already tried everything he knows and would have already improved his printing if he could have. Micah had difficulties with his hand coordination. Micah and your unique learner are not lazy.

The truth behind Micah's writing problem was much more complex. Not only did he have difficulty spacing letters, shaping letters and placing them on the lines of a page, but he also had hand muscle weakness. Micah's doctor explained to his mother that Micah had delays in fine motor muscle development. With these problems, one can now see that Micah was giving his best effort. As he matured, Micah was also giving into his frustrations.

Micah had problems with his ability to sense gravity correctly operating on his body through his vestibular* (V) system, his ability to make his muscles do what his brain believed needed to be done through his proprioceptive* (P) system, and his sense of touch through his tactile* (T) system. With VPT* deficiencies, Micah had trouble coordinating his large tetherball muscles as well as his small pencil-holding muscles.

The most obvious issue that Micah had with writing was incorrectly shaping his letters. The same letter would be misshaped multiple ways with no apparent pattern to letter formation. In printing the same letter repeatedly in the context of a five-sentence paragraph, the same letter was circled by the teacher in red with the comment, "Incorrectly printed in four or five different styles of wrong. Please redo."

When writing in Micah's daily language arts journal, the lowercase letter "r" would be written backward or it would be hard to read, appearing like the letter "v" or looking like a lowercase "n" or a lowercase "t." All these varieties appeared within a single paragraph. Some letters were formed correctly, yet the majority of letters were illegible. The teacher would attempt to decipher the letters and words but it was hard to do. Micah did not place spaces between his words and they were crowded and bunched up at the end of the line. He did not orient his letters correctly on the horizontal lines of the paper. Random floating letters and crowded words made it very, very hard to decipher, even for him.

Printing a sentence and planning for space on the line require the same understanding for planning space on a playground. Playground equipment provides experiences for school children to plan and navigate space through body movements. Planning to move the body under the slide, through the tunnel and over the bridge are examples of physically navigating through three-dimensional space. Micah's unfortunate misuse of space on the playground and the tetherball court, by either being too close to the ball or too far away, was a deficiency in three-dimensional use of space. Micah's difficulties with three-dimensional space were mirrored in his difficulties processing two-dimensional space while in the classroom attempting to print.

For the human eye, blank space between words is imperative for reading accuracy. The eye becomes accustomed to the horizontal skyline that the shape of a word occupies on the page. Try deciphering a doctor's handwritten directions on a prescription. The clues are in the actual shape of the word, indicating the number of letters as well as the space between the words and by noting any letters that hang below the horizontal line of the paper, such as a lower case letter "g," and those that extend above, such as a "t." Spacing of each word and line orientation of each letter are as important as correctly shaping the letters. Printing words requires the ability to process three-dimensional space and translate this knowledge to printing in two-dimensional space. This perceptual skill is referred to as spatial awareness*.

In addition to requiring accurate spatial awareness, fine motor tasks also require accurate data from the entire sensory system*. The sensory system provides incoming data to the brain through the feel of the pencil and through the visual results of the physical

* See Glossary for definition

act of printing. The sensory information informs the brain and the brain informs the muscles. This feedback loop allows for a back and forth playback to correct errors and to modify the work as the printing task progresses. Modifications such as printing heavier, printing smaller, or better placement of the letters on the line are all accomplished through the ongoing feedback loop between the sensory-motor system* pathways. When the visual sensory system picks up that the printing is too light, then the motor system will make the physical adjustments to press the pencil more firmly on the paper.

The motor system and its muscles are in charge of the physical skill of recruiting the correct muscles to do the correct job. This can power the pencil downward to print or can lift the pencil up off the page to create the spaces. The motor system provides the joints and muscles with information coming from the brain to allow the individual the ability to move and function. If the feedback from the muscles informs the brain that the pencil is being held too lightly, then an intact brain and body system would communicate to the hand and say, "Hold the pencil tighter and press down more firmly."

The motor system involved in successful pencil control can be considered a fundamental building block. Legible printing incorporates a balance between the strength of the muscles of the wrist and the smooth nimbleness, finesse and control of the fingers. Letter formation is a high-level advancement in fine motor coordination. Writing or printing is a highly choreographed physical act. The use of a writing utensil incorporates a profound level of physical muscle maturation. It is a true developmental leap.

Legible printing also requires stable postural control and good eye/hand coordination. Printing requires the writing arm to be able to float across the paper. If lack of postural control is a problem, the individual will sit in a rounded and collapsed forward posture with the face directed downward. In this posture they might look disinterested, but you need to look more closely as that might not be the case at all. Poor postural control is usually the true cause for printing problems, not disinterest.

Much like a ski racer is taught to perceive each ski as an extension of their own foot, the student must extend the perception* of their hand to include the writing utensil. The child must not only have an internal concept of their own hand and its ability to move, grasp, pinch, and perform actions, but also to be able to extend this concept to hold a tool in the hand for precise use. If you don't know where your body begins and ends, you'll have a very difficult time extending the parameters of your body to include a pencil, an eating utensil, a joystick for video games, a computer mouse, or a pair of skis when downhill racing.

Earlier in this chapter, the reader envisioned driving along a curvy mountain road in a large and unfamiliar vehicle while towing a trailer. This provided an example of trying to move and function correctly without knowing the parameters of your own body. The driver didn't know where the sides and the back of the trailer were when handling curves on the road. The driver didn't know where the vehicle began and ended.

When you have a good understanding of your own vehicle's size, you can correct your car easily because the vehicle is familiar to you. An individual with a healthy sense of their body can initiate an action, observe the results, and alter the next course of action to improve the outcome. They know their body and what it can do. Errors on the tetherball court and errors in printing can be self-identified and corrected for those with a correctly functioning VPT. Through the give and take strategy of ongoing observing and modifying the technique to improve the finished product, the typical student can productively work until the task is completed correctly. Not so with unique learners.

* See Glossary for definition

Micah's poorly developed VPT sensory processing systems* did not allow for an automatic and naturally occurring self-check system. He needed an alternative strategy to get the job done. Micah needed to make fewer errors to improve his grades. As an initial step, it became clear that he really needed to develop the skill of double checking all of his work.

The school team, including Micah's parents, elected to make double-checking procedures a priority. These procedures were so important to his success that Micah was allowed to do a smaller quantity of work in order to gain in quality of work. Micah was permitted to do only 80 percent of the worksheets. If there were ten problems, Micah was tested on only eight, but he was expected to double-check all his work.

Gradually, this high priority strategy of double-checking began to pay off. Micah would diligently "check and redo", making corrections for every problem that showed a "whoops-a-daisy." Eventually, he could independently see where errors were made and correct them himself. Through this process, Micah got more and more answers correct.

A long-term strategy was identified by his teacher. When Micah started to hand in the 80 percent complete worksheets with no errors, he would be encouraged to perform 90 percent of the assignment and then 100 percent. However, while this improved the quality of Micah's work, it did little to change the underlying problems with his VPT systems. For example, the amount of printing was hard for Micah. He became easily fatigued and complained about his sore hand. Unfortunately, his ability to use his pencil was not very efficient.

Learning to accurately control the muscles and to vary or grade the amount of muscle contraction is yet another developmental milestone. Some muscles hold still and stabilize as other muscles move. The child must learn the exact amount of speed and muscle thrust required when grasping a feather found on the grass versus a rock. An ice cream cone handed from the ice cream vendor requires a different grasp response than a friend handing over a baseball.

The body is constantly interacting with the VPT and the rest of the sensory system. The body and brain collaborate on this data with the person's interpretation of their immediate environment to know exactly how quickly, slowly, strongly or lightly the muscles must be employed to successfully interact with the world. Tossing a ball to Mommy sitting close by the child versus tossing the ball to Daddy across the entire back yard requires a different action of the muscle and joint system.

Micah tended to have an all or nothing response to his muscles. When he attempted to share his eraser with a student at the next desk, he tossed it onto his neighbor's desk but threw it too hard. Micah accidentally hit another student. The teacher's time-out consequence, imposed for throwing objects during a lesson, further confused and stressed Micah. It led to a breakdown in his performance. His ability to participate in the classroom was greatly compromised due to his feelings of embarrassment and confusion.

Other students who have a good internal understanding of their muscles and joints can and should be held accountable for inappropriately throwing an item in the classroom. It is safe to assume that if these more physically coordinated students throw the eraser hard, it is intentional. Premeditated eraser throwing was not Micah's forte. He didn't plan to hit the student. It was an accident.

Students like Micah may interpret the teacher's punishment to mean "never share an eraser." They may inappropriately shutdown from all classroom participation for a period of time. The shutdown response is their strategy for processing the confusing event, but it can keep a child from participating in other important events. The withdrawal or shutdown even encompasses activities they might normally enjoy. It can be confusing when the child chooses to miss an event that most would consider fun, but sometimes when this shutdown occurs the child's only strategy is to withdraw from every activity.

In addition to the compassionate and knowledgeable teachers already in his life, Micah needed a program to help him better gauge his muscle activity. The OT* program was provided in collaboration with Micah's PE teacher. Activities for students to practice grading how soft or hard and slow or fast the muscles needed to function for accuracy was practiced with enthusiasm by the entire PE class. During the warm-up PE exercises, sets of 10 movement activities were developed by the students. These muscle coordination exercises are depicted in the "Strategies to Try" section at the end of this chapter.

The PE exercises were coupled with hand strengthening exercises. Wall push-ups were taught for home. Classroom friendly seated chair press-ups (that involved pushing up through Micah's hands while he was seated at his school desk) were encouraged every period. Weight bearing through the hands by wall push-ups and seated press-ups; are both OT strategies to reproduce the natural developmental stage that stimulates hand maturation leading to more complex hand function.

The fine motor skill required for precise work, such as using a screwdriver, a toothbrush, threading a needle and printing legibly, results from the integration of multiple sensory systems. For example, the visual input and sense of touch are linked to the student's memory in order to understand the correct feeling applied to the writing utensil. Muscle and joint position sense is required in order to maintain an age-appropriate grasp of the tool. In addition, the huge muscles that support our posture in upright sitting require profound coordination and stabilization.

The muscles and postural sense registered in the brain must continually integrate information regarding the student's seated or standing posture in relationship to gravity. The muscles must control the trunk to maintain the body in a stable posture. This is necessary for the nuances of printing control to occur way down the movement chain to the hand, thumb, and fingers. In addition to the importance of correct posture, the visual system must continually process information to zoom in on the correct target. The visual system must filter out other competing visual stimuli in order to allow the student to concentrate.

The body must be still for the eyes to work well. The eyes must focus on the horizontal lines of the page, the shape of each letter and the space between words. The student's eyes must stay very focused to not lose their place and cause extra effort and errors. Challenges in any portion of the sensory system can result in the student needing to apply extra concentration and effort to compensate for the diminished sensory processing*.

Not surprisingly, Micah constantly described being tired. For Micah, copying a five-letter word that the teacher wrote on the front board required an extreme amount of attention and energy expenditure as compared to the average student in his class. Generating his own ideas to write without copying from a model required even more effort. Thinking of the correct answer and printing it within a set time frame required an almost insurmountable amount of energy expenditure. Complaining of being tired and appearing physically fatigued can be a red flag for children and students with poor sensory processing.

Lauren was another student exhibiting fatigue while seated at her desk. The teacher requested an academic-related OT* evaluation due to Lauren's obvious collapsed posture and her poor writing skills. I interviewed the teacher and her parents and observed Lauren in a variety of school settings.

Lauren was an eager member of the sixth-grade basketball team. She correctly characterized herself as the best free thrower on the team. Friends and family cheered Lauren's performance. Her young, athletic physique together with her blonde hair pulled back in a ponytail and large bright eyes focusing on the hoop were all a joy to see. It was easy to get caught up in her high-energy action.

In the classroom, Lauren's large bright eyes easily solicited assistance from adults and classmates when Lauren experienced trouble with her schoolwork. Lauren was a child cancer survivor. Significant portions of her childhood were spent in medical settings. Her childhood development was challenged by weakness and lethargy typical of this form of disease. The drastic treatment and medications healed the disease but caused reduced nerve conduction to the tips of her fingers. Lauren had difficulty feeling the pencil, controlling scissors, and managing buttons and fasteners.

The doctors believed the lack of sensation in the fingers would be reversible over time. The weakness and lethargy early in Lauren's childhood, however, prevented her from achieving typical developmental milestones, such as age-appropriate crawling.

Crawling is very important in hand development. The weight bearing provides the motor cortex* with a heightened sense of the position and function of the small joints and the hand muscles. As the brain's understanding of the hand is enhanced, the grasp action becomes more refined. The grasp moves to a three-finger grasp and eventually a two-finger grasp via the thumb and index finger. This is the fine motor grasp that is needed to hold a pencil properly by second grade.

In sixth grade, Lauren tended to lean on her elbow while attempting to write with the same hand. Instead of allowing it to float across the page, the arm acted as a pillar. The hand was inappropriately anchored by the weight-bearing elbow. The primary function of her right, dominant, printing arm became

* See Glossary for definition

one of physically supporting her and holding her upright against gravity. The cost to Lauren of developing this unfortunate strategy due to lack of postural muscle strength was illegible writing. Her poor posture resulted in her inability to easily recruit the correct muscles and joints to print the complex loops and other nuances necessary to shape the letters of the English language. In sixth grade the narrow lines on the page added a new challenge to Lauren's fine motor coordination.

For the hand and fingers to function efficiently, many developmental building blocks need to be in place. Hand maturation occurs through a developmental sequence starting in infancy. The infant begins this process by orally exploring the hand in his or her mouth. Acknowledging the existence of their hands and facilitating the tactile responses with this oral input allows the hands to be better understood by the infant and eventually be used for securing toys. This leads to visually looking at the hand and is a developmental building block necessary for early eye/hand control. Grasp of an item initially tends to be performed in a gross "raking" motion whereby all the fingers fold over the palm of the hand. Intentional grasp and release is actually a relatively high-level motor milestone and begins to emerge around the time an infant learns to crawl. Infants love to pass you their toy at this stage.

In OT, we understand that the fine motor control of a pencil or crayon needs the fingers to be free to move and wiggle while the wrist is firmly held in a static* posture. Asking the wrist to do one thing (remain still) and asking the fingers to perform a different action (wiggle) is a tremendous challenge. However, this is a milestone that must be in place prior to efficient printing. For correct printing and writing, the wrist remains still and only the small finger joints move. A relaxed elbow and nimble fingers are complemented by a stable wrist that is maintained in a mid-position.

* See Glossary for definition

If the child or adult has not acquired this developmental milestone, they will have a stiff wrist and their fingers will be held in an inappropriately stiff four-finger grasp. Some teachers call this a "fisted grasp." In this developmentally immature hand, the crayon or pencil held in the inappropriately stiff hand moves across the page by motion powered at the elbow. Coloring or printing that relies on motion originating from the elbow utilizes muscles that are too large for precise work. These large muscles are unable to accommodate the highly targeted task of coloring between the lines or the highly skilled task of printing. Often these students can only draw when standing. Once their hand matures and the pencil grasp becomes more functional, these students can be expected to print while seated. Keep in mind that if "brain working here*" productive behaviors are evident, then any posture can be considered acceptable, within reason.

A writing utensil is different from an eating utensil. The use of an eating utensil requires a different hand posture. When using a fork or spoon, the fingers are maintained in a static and locked position while the wrist is allowed to move. Picture the action required to successfully use a soup spoon. The fingers stay still and the wrist rotates and moves. Use of a writing utensil requires the opposite: the fingers move and the wrist stays still. Differentiation* of the wrist and finger muscles requires successful developmental muscle control.

An OT exercise program was established to work on improving hand function. Both Lauren and Micah were students who had poor fine motor control for different reasons. Lauren had lost her sense of touch in her fingertips. Micah poorly sensed and poorly coordinated his fingers due to sensory integration* challenges. Because of her reduced sense of touch, Lauren needed to "bombard" her brain with input of various textures and materials through the fingertips and hands. These OT exercises that focused on tactile input were also very beneficial for Micah who struggled in identifying the correct amount of pressure to apply to the pencil and the correct muscle coordination for sustained printing.

Both students were given a home exercise program to work on their posture and their sense of touch. A program for improving poor posture and for developing printing skills is outlined in the "Strategies to Try" section at the end of this chapter.

Thanks to Lauren's highly motivated parents, over time and with dedicated practice, Lauren began to develop independence in handling buttons, zippers, and fasteners. Previously, when her fingers couldn't finesse open the snack cracker and cheese wrappers, Lauren would use her teeth. This was a clear indicator of her difficulties with fine motor control. Gradually, fewer teeth marks appeared on the lids of her re-useable plastic food containers. Adults in the school cafeteria were less frequently asked to help her open containers and juice boxes.

Thanks to Micah's self-motivation, he began to lead the PE class in "brain/body" warm-up exercises. His parents enrolled him in a martial arts class and he incorporated some of the graceful body actions of this discipline in his PE warm-up program. Though he never did return to tetherball, he discovered that he was better suited to science club activities for socializing and martial arts for exercising.

Micah's and Lauren's OT programs were aimed to promote real change in their classroom abilities. The developmental milestones of hand function can be fairly predictable and are invaluable in assessing and treating a child's fine motor problem. Both students progressed through the natural sequence of typical hand development.

Maturation that promotes integration of the entire sensory system is the key to success in helping a child learn how to learn. When sensory-motor integration is patchy or irregular, learning problems frequently occur. Problems may present as difficulty in math, writing, or reading. To improve classroom performance, attention must be focused on facilitating the patchy sensory system. Multisensory* solutions for gross motor* and fine motor problems have been introduced in these past two chapters. Multisensory solutions to reading problems will be outlined in detail in the next chapter. The following section on immediate solutions for fine motor problems will help unique learners with diminished fine motor control as well as with gross motor control.

STRATEGIES TO TRY

IF your child or student tends to make a lot of mistakes when printing,

THEN when it comes to printing for schoolwork, establish a double-check system and allow your child sufficient time to check over their work to correct for any mistakes. Start by having your child look for any incorrectly formed letters. They can circle or highlight them. That may be enough for the first stage. You can make the corrections together. Try not to overwhelm and frustrate your child with this task. Consider initially lowering the amount of work your student does so that he or she can focus on quality without feeling too pressured by the volume of work.

IF your child or student seems to hold their pencil incorrectly, either too loosely or too tightly, or throws a ball in your direction much too hard because your child doesn't seem to realize that you are right next to them, or if they handle buttons and fasteners so roughly that they break,

THEN they need help better gauging their muscle activity. Exercises to help this type of muscle coordination problem can be done in groups at school, such as PE time, as well as individually between homework demands. The following exercises are very helpful:

Work to establish a rhythm for repetitive jumping or jumping with clapping. Try sequencing a series of motions such as stomping, clapping, and jumping that are followed by shrugging the shoulders.

Put together a program of 10 standing wall push-ups, 10 standing arm crosses with opposite hands gently tugging on the ear lobes, 10 seated chair press-ups, and 10 squishes of the palms, and finish with clapping at chest level while jumping at the exact same moment.

Encourage weight-bearing through the hands by performing floor, wall and seated push-ups.

Try crawling races, wheelbarrow relays* and other exercises to promote action in the large muscle groups. These help the background muscles do the right thing for precise motor control to occur.

Pulling on the earlobes and along the length of the ear may seem to be a funny exercise, but it's very effective to help with this refined muscle coordination problem.

Squishing the palms of the hands together for a count of five and repeating five times also helps a child feel and apply the correct amount of muscle strength. Squish with hands overhead, to the side, behind, or wherever the child invents.

IF your child has poor posture and is often slumped over their desk or propping up their head with their hand,

THEN they are likely lacking core and postural muscle strength. Fun activities to strengthen the core muscles can include performing a crawling activity with a teddy bear or other item placed on the child's back in order to stay steady and keeping the back straight while moving. A different activity done in standing involves tapping a balloon overhead. Raising the arms up can help a child develop core muscle strength. Gradually utilize a heavier item, even a weighted ball or heavy beanbag.

IF your child or student has difficulty printing and the product is below grade-level expectation,

THEN examples of everyday activities to promote hand function are as follows:

Assist with meal preparation: wash vegetables, break broccoli apart, set the table, fill glasses by pouring from a jug.

Perform household chores: carry items (such as taking out the trash or bringing in groceries, putting groceries away), fold towels, utilize containers with different types of fasteners to maintain a neat bedroom.

Use playground and sports equipment: climb and swing on

bars, play with ropes, use bats and balls, or play games like wall ball.

Practice using eating utensils correctly and use a knife and fork to cut soft items. Some games, such as relay races with cotton balls held carefully on a spoon, can be enjoyable and helpful.

Promote finger dexterity: play an instrument, practice typing on a computer, bake, do carpentry, fasten nuts on screws, play card games, use an eye dropper to transfer water from one container to another.

Wash hands while looking at the hands, soap, rinse, and dry each finger.

Use different size writing utensils such as golf pencils, different pencil grips, and pens with bumpy surfaces.

Feel with the hands inside a sensory box. Use rice grains or dried beans in a small box with some objects hidden in the rice so that the child's fingers must search them out.

Explore a variety of materials. Use finger paints, paper mache; move the hands through the dirt while gardening.

CHAPTER SEVEN

READING TO LEARN: DEALING WITH READING PROBLEMS

Noah could play baseball and basketball, and he was on the school running club. His family was very active. They enjoyed outdoor adventures. Noah often assisted his mother during her competitions in local marathons. Noah was a very physically capable fourth-grade boy. It seemed odd to each of them, especially to Noah, that he just couldn't read!

Many students have a profound reading problem but show average intelligence in other aspects of learning. Like Noah, they are adept at specific physical abilities, sports, art, or building construction. Dyslexia* is a learning disorder characterized by trouble reading despite normal intelligence. Frequently, students like Noah have an excellent auditory memory and can easily recall song lyrics or movie lines.

Since he began school, however, Noah had difficulty remembering the actual names and the sounds made by each letter. He also had difficulty remembering the shape of each letter when printing. During his earlier years at school, huge alphabet letters were displayed on the walls with pictures of animals and other objects related to each letter. A classic xylophone reminded students of the letter "x," an elephant for "e," snake for "s," and a zebra for "z."

As the students progressed from one grade level to the next, the pictures were removed. By third grade, just the upper and lower case letters would be displayed. The alphabet was placed on a long banner at the front of the room. By fourth grade, small alphabet cards were laminated and adhered to each student's desktop. Noah referenced the alphabet card on a constant basis.

Noah's parents first recognized their son's difficulty reading letters and words when he was unable to find his assigned seat 10G in a local concert hall. Noah's parents described Noah looking at each seat in the tenth row using a very disorganized method. He walked back and forth from seat A to D and then skipped the middle section and started hunting for his seat from M to seat S. "Where are you going?" "What are you doing?" Noah's parents echoed to him. Noah just sat down where he was. Assuming Noah was making a choice to sit away from his family, Noah became the source of his family's humor and teasing. Just sitting down in any seat was the only way Noah could think of to minimize the embarrassing scrutiny: "Better they think I was just joking around…" Noah was learning how to conceal his reading problem.

By fourth grade, Noah felt very stuck. It was as though he awoke one morning to find his friends and peers miles ahead of him in school. He was often required to stay in at recess to finish a class assignment. His friends found other basketball players to play on their teams as Noah was always starting too late for recess games. As a result, Noah quickly became disinterested in school.

Traditionally, up until fourth grade, students are expected to learn to read. However, in fourth grade suddenly the expectation is for students to "read to learn." The amount of reading required for every subject goes up dramatically. Students are expected to read independently and to fully comprehend the stories. They are taught to synthesize the plot and characters in order to sequence the events and to identify possible outcomes. The comprehension questions become more and more complex.

Noah's teachers saw his grades decline and responded immediately by finding experts at school to provide reading lessons in small group settings. Smaller groups and individualized learning goals seemed to be helping Noah just "squeak through" his fourth-grade curriculum demands.

Noah became acutely aware of the difference between himself and his classmates. The distress of feeling different affected Noah's drive to learn. A student's drive to learn and their emotional response to learning greatly impact their performance. Learning occurs easily only in certain instances. A support team to help Noah needed to be in place and an OT* evaluation was recommended. This process was timed perfectly. Much greater delay and Noah's self-confidence and joy of his school life would have been at risk for long-term damage.

During the OT evaluation, it became clear that Noah could not recall many of the letters of the alphabet. He had memorized the sequence by singing the alphabet song but needed to use an alphabet card whenever printing letters and words. Physically, he was capable of holding the pencil in an age-appropriate manner with good fine motor* dexterity. His posture was excellent and he used his left, non-dominant hand to support the page for printing. Actually printing the letters correctly, however, was a very difficult task. Reading was even more difficult.

Noah's confusion with letters limited his ability to advance forward in his school work. Although Noah was in fourth grade, he had difficulty reading common words more characteristic of a student at a first-grade level. Reading basic text such as 3- and 4-word sentences or any kind of timed reading tasks were very difficult for him.

At the time of initiating OT, reading was so difficult for Noah that he had to be convinced that reading and writing had any value in his life at all. His teacher told me that Noah liked history and, with some prompting, he showed enthusiasm for studying anything remotely history-related. As a result, Noah and I began to study the history of written communication. I believed that Noah needed to feel the necessity for written communication in his own life in order to overcome his feelings of inadequacy. I hoped that he could find the inspiration to apply new effort to learning by studying the difficulties man, earlier in our society, overcame to communicate in this advanced fashion.

Early in our society, the development of written language took a long, long time to master. The extreme difficulty of this complex skill was overridden by the necessity and strong desire to communicate through drawings and letter symbols. Reading and writing began at a period of human history when travel had become more common. With the growth of long-distance trade, reliable communication and record keeping became necessary. Through Noah's computer search, he learned that the development of writing began in Asia, the Near East, and Mesoamerica. Very early in human history, up until the development of community living, the human brain was primarily focused on ensuring the survival of the members of the group. The brain was not focused on developing the specialized skill of reading and writing until human culture had advanced and the technology had been developed, be it stone and tablet, pencil and paper, or mouse and computer.

For survival purposes, human beings early in society tended to focus more on balance, by detecting and responding to gravity through the vestibular system*, as well as the ability to move effectively through the action of the proprioceptive system*. These survival skills were seen as more culturally necessary than learning to read.

* See Glossary for definition

Learning to read, even to this day, remains very dependent upon the foundational skills of balance, movement, and touch. In fact, the senses of balance, movement and touch affect the correct development of the visual system. With the sensory system* integrated and processing information well, the visual system can discern and decode symbols, such as letters and numerals. The eye muscles are dependent on steady balance to be able to track and to discriminate small targets. Good balance is based on a healthy vestibular system.

The ability to move is dependent upon a healthy proprioceptive (P) system. These balance and movement sensations are augmented by the sense of touch (T). Correctly operating VPT* sensory systems allows the visual system to continuously order and sort stimuli coming into the eye. The sense of touch gives order to the incoming sensory data. Integration of this sensory data allows for the development of reading, writing, and arithmetic.

During Noah's OT session, we designed a home and school program that incorporated balance and movement activities together with eye-tracking exercises. Noah's parents and his teacher received a copy of the exercises that incorporated the use of reading material with unusual reading postures to improve eye-tracking. The exercises are depicted in the "Strategies to Try" section at the end of this chapter.

Other visual motor exercises helped strengthen Noah's eye-tracking ability, such as a "maze" worksheet navigated with a pencil, finding a hidden picture, connect the dots, word search exercises, and tracking a single line out of a series of lines (that looked like a plate of spaghetti lines on a page) in order to find the correct endpoint. Performing these exercises in a variety of different postures was helpful.

Noah was an adventuresome fourth-grade student. Prior to his drop in grades, he was very confident and very athletically competent. Lack of reading ability, however, had a negative effect on his self-esteem. Once he became aware of his progress through the OT exercises, he became enthusiastic once again and developed creative ways to help his eyes better discern letters and words for reading. Not all students appreciate the value of reading exercises and strategies. Without a student's interest aroused, it becomes very hard to teach new skills and new ways of doing old skills.

In contrast to Noah, Jake was a very hard-to-teach student. Perhaps Jake's tough-guy physical demeanor was one of the reasons he seemed to fall through the cracks. He had been through a number of his parent's separations, reunions, and repeat separations. Further, one of his parents was incarcerated for a time. Jake looked as though he was fed up. Although he tried to use humor to disguise his academic weakness, in ninth grade his teachers viewed him as defiant. No one guessed that what he actually had was a learning problem.

Jake's teachers were focused on Jake's poor behavior rather than considering any other possible source for his academic woes. While the teachers' assumptions actually made Jake's problem worse, it was hard to blame them for jumping to conclusions. Jake's posture was collapsed over his desk. He was angry and short-tempered toward anyone asking him to sit up straight. Frequently, self-deprecating remarks were muttered: "I'm an idiot."

Jake resorted to tactics to avoid the discovery of incomplete work. Frequently he would use humor, preferring to be seen as the class clown rather than an un-proficient student. This type of behavioral strategy alienated his educational team. Jake's friends, however, loved the comic relief and egged him on to be funny, a psychological reward that was strengthening his avoidance tactics.

Jake's dad wasn't laughing. He called a meeting for all his son's ninth-grade teachers and the high school principal. Jake's dad could not understand why his son's grades were plummeting. When Jake joined the latter half of the meeting, he was uncomfortably barraged with question after question. The school team wanted to know why Jake was not working to his potential. His dad wondered if Jake had involved himself with "the wrong crowd." Jake had developed an indifferent attitude toward his performance.

The meeting adjourned with the agreement that all parties would oversee Jake's effort. His dad agreed to initial Jake's homework. The teachers agreed to communicate by e-mail when Jake failed to complete an assignment or received a poor grade. In order to be thorough, an academic-related OT* evaluation was requested to identify strategies for better handwriting. Despite the team's plan, Jake's father and his teachers all believed Jake just needed to try harder and stop misbehaving.

The OT evaluation comprised a teacher interview, classroom observation and one-on-one school-related OT testing. During the observation portion of the evaluation, reduced visual-motor* control was noted. For example, when Jake was reading, he needed to turn at his neck in order to scan the text on the page. By this age, normally the head stays still and the eyes track on their own. It became clear that most directly related to Jake's handwriting fiasco was his inability to move his eyes correctly.

Visual-motor control, the ability of the eye muscles to move correctly, is dependent upon the stability of the head while it sits on the neck. The stability of the neck is dependent on the stability of the body. Without this stability, focusing on a small target, like a letter in any word, is extremely difficult.

Jake had not yet achieved the developmental skill of differentiating* his eye muscles from that of his head and neck. When I tested Jake's ability to track his eyes horizontally, such as watching the end of my pencil move left to right across his near-visual range, Jake would turn at the head and neck versus displaying the more age-appropriate skill of tracking with the small muscles of the eyes and keeping the head and neck still.

During the classroom observation time, I could see that looking up at the front board was problematic for Jake. Because he was unable to move his eye muscles independently from his neck muscles, visually locking onto a target was difficult. Without the stability of his body, errors frequently occurred. Jake would copy the wrong words.

I watched Jake nod his head up and down each time he copied a word or some numerals from the front board. Other students could glance their eyes upward while holding their head cast downward toward the paper on their desk. In this way, they could keep their place more easily and not become visually lost. Jake, however, with his need to nod his entire head up and down, would frequently look down and discover that he had lost his visual target on the page. To do this task, Jake was physically working at a much higher level than his peers. When he complained of being fatigued, it was an accurate statement. The labor-intensive strategies this student was required to use to overcome visual deficits were truly exhausting him.

Students who are unable to view a horizontally moving object across their near visual field without also moving at the head and neck will have difficulty writing. It is essential to keep the head and body still while the visual system tracks the printing activity. Slow speed of printing as well as frequent errors can usually be attributed to a student who is unable to move the small eye muscles independent of the head and neck muscles.

Many times this particular learning challenge does not fully present itself to the student, parents and teachers until third or fourth grade when the arithmetic computations begin to incorporate two and three digit equations and when reading intensity increases.

Writing out a complex arithmetic equation and reading efficiently, require visually perceiving space. Visual-spatial awareness* in the three-dimensional world is that skill necessary to navigate through a busy classroom successfully without bumping into other students, furniture, or objects on the floor. Moving within this real-world obstacle course requires a reliable visual system that can also perceive the exact amount of space required for the body to navigate as well as the relative time required to move from one area of the classroom to another. This appreciation for moving in space is considered an aspect of visual-spatial awareness. The classroom provides a three-dimensional opportunity to explore spatial awareness. Printing on a two-dimensional piece of paper requires an even more sophisticated skill set.

Most students would be expected to focus on completing a worksheet with the correct answer written in their best quality of writing. Students like Jake, however, can get lost in the lines and spaces. These students get lost in the physical process of writing and printing. They can become easily frustrated.

The OT findings allowed Jake's teacher to see the problem from Jake's perspective. As a result, Jake was given an extra sheet of lined paper and taught how to complete his work using the additional page. It is surprising how often the quantity of lines and spaces made available on worksheets and job applications can influence the ability to be successful in providing a coherent written response.

In OT, we know that better sensory integration* leads to better learning. Letting a student experience spatial directions (left, right, up, down) and the physical dimensions of their own body through the interpretation of movement, touch, and vision promotes the integration of the sensory system. Learning these concepts through improvement in sensory integration is more helpful in the long term than relying on memorization strategies, tricks, or rules.

Difficulty reading is a huge and pervasive problem. Looking at letters and words requires a correctly operating sense of vision. The visual system is dependent on the body's ability to detect gravity and movement as well as on correct tactile processing. The tactile system* helps to give meaning to objects and to establish categories and patterns leading to logical reasoning, learning and intelligence.

Memorization and recalling rules can be very costly in terms of energy expenditure required to recall the trick or the rule. Often it requires ideal circumstances to remember and to perform the trick correctly. The students who rely on memorization for basic concepts can be observed in the classroom as trying to control their environment: "Shh, I'm trying to remember!" These students can be highly sensitive to distractions and appear to discontinue working before full effort has been applied. Little known to the adult, this reader has tried very, very hard before quitting the task. Quitting frequently is the student's best coping mechanism to prevent further disorganization and lack of mental coherence*. Often, they sincerely want to learn and they know that getting frustrated does not help learning.

I established an exercise program for Jake to improve his eye muscle movement while keeping the head still. The visual–motor program was based on the natural developmental sequence of eye control. It was hoped that by following the naturally expected course of development, Jake could gradually build on all the body systems necessary to promote correct eye tracking. Through this developmental sequence, it was hoped that his eye muscle problem could be minimized.

One of Jake's home exercises was to watch TV while lying on his tummy and lifting his head up by supporting his weight through his elbows and, eventually, through his hands. This exercise was then further progressed by having Jake use a therapy

* See Glossary for definition

ball* under his tummy while lifting both legs off the ground. These and other specific exercise ideas are in the "Strategies to Try" section at the end of this chapter.

All of Jake's exercises aimed to reproduce the natural developmental milestones that normally allow the eye muscles to work separately from the head and neck muscles early in childhood development. Tummy lying, for an infant who raises their head way up high, triggers the muscles that work the eyes. Various combinations of these developmental exercises helped strengthen Jake's visual system and these exercises are also outlined in the "Strategies to Try" section at the end of this chapter.

Occupational therapists* will use a metronome to assist unique learners to complete tasks within a specific rhythm and with a consistent sense of timing. At home, the metronome can be employed for accurate timing while spelling words, clapping and stomping rhythms or stating the alphabet backward. Daily chores should follow patterns: things to clean-up in the kitchen first, and then wash up and double-check homework before school. A rhythm reduces strain and potential for errors. Yes, take the trash out into the large outdoor bin every morning (whether it needs it or not). An internal rhythm, a code, a pattern is necessary for efficient reading.

In addition to following a developmental sequence to facilitate the visual system, much of Jake's school OT program was based on principles of neuroplasticity*. Jake was helped to realize that the brain can grow and change itself with proper exercise and with proper nourishment. The brain is made up of many pathways. Cognitive strengths can be viewed as healthy muscles and these muscles recruit new pathways throughout the brain. The brain can become stronger.

Ever since science discovered that the brain circuitry could be re-modeled well into the golden sunset of adult years, products

* See Glossary for definition

for memory restoration have become abundant. There is a surge of high-tech programs that improve brain activity. The research is irrefutable. Brain activity increases in senior citizens, grades for students improve, as evidenced through double-blind studies. Brain studies show tissues that "light up" when older adults played the latest memory-enhancing game. This is fortunate for adults wanting to learn new skills later in life, like Nigel.

Nigel was a restaurant chef in the winter, a jack of all trades at various local helicopter ski mountain resorts in the spring, and a carpenter in the summer and fall. Nigel and his wife enjoyed travel all over the Pacific Northwest to ski resorts and to visit clients and friends in distant locations. My husband and I met him skiing. Over cocoa in the ski lounge, Nigel described his interesting life. His start as a young man would not have suggested a future with such rich experiences and job success. At one time in his life, Nigel just could not read.

At school, Nigel slipped through the cracks and entered adulthood with a bare minimum of reading ability. This can happen with affable children and I could easily imagine that he was as personable as a child as he was over cocoa between ski runs together. Fortunately for Nigel, due to neuroplasticity, it wasn't too late for him to improve his reading.

As a younger child, Nigel described that his poor reading was more than just a handicap; it was an embarrassing handicap. Nigel found his strength through sports and through his engaging personality and genuine enjoyment of others. When older, he discovered friendships with fellow restaurateurs, skiers, and soccer teammates. As an adult, Nigel was invited by a helicopter ski company to join their guests in pristine winter and spring ski terrain. Nigel was known to be the most reliable of workers. He took his responsibilities seriously. Nigel respected others and enjoyed an immense scattering of friends across the globe.

Nigel's method of speaking was joyful and entertaining. He spoke with an obvious social intelligence; he knew his audience. While telling me his story, his varied facial expressions, with an occasional raised eyebrow and change in his volume of speaking together with his posture, all held me spellbound and captivated. Nigel truly had figured out that communication includes both spoken and unspoken messages.

Nigel learned early in his life to rely on nonverbal cues. As an adult, his work required interacting with people from all over the world. No matter who he spoke to, Nigel was aware of the individual idiosyncrasies of attitude, body language, voice, and use of language that were characteristic of the people he met. Nigel knew that we convey our attitudes and our beliefs in every word, movement, and gesture. If we remain silent, our silence and other nonverbal communications "speak" for us.

With Nigel's sophistication in blending the nonverbal communication with the verbal, his reading problems never hindered him as a young adult entering the work force. He ensured that he understood the nature of his work responsibilities at the beginning of each day by meeting with his boss. His limited reading abilities did not get in his way even during his summer work that involved building planning and construction.

Later in life Nigel took on the skill of improving his reading and writing skills in the same dedicated manner as his other responsibilities. Nigel continues to be one of the few who handwrites a unique and personalized letter on his annual Christmas cards. He described his process; "In mid-October, I begin writing the letters. I imagine each friend sitting in front of me and then I carefully fill the card with stories I want that friend to know." When was the last time you sent Christmas cards with handwritten letters?

Nigel was tutored by the love of his life, his wife. They found strategies unique to Nigel's learning style to help him improve his reading skills. Although he thinks that he may read a little slower than some, Nigel knows he has no deficits in reading comprehension. He reads newspapers and news magazines from cover to cover.

Noah, Jake and Nigel were able to experience profound degrees of improvement. Noah combined his athletic ability with a newfound interest in learning to read. He took on the challenge of reading like a true competitor and used his athleticism to incorporate reading exercises with specific movements. His reading practices became quite physical and he was always achieving "personal bests."

Jake strengthened his visual system and he no longer needed to rely on inappropriate strategies such as ill-timed humor or task avoidance. By changing his brain's capacity to learn, it became possible to circumvent missing developmental building blocks. He found he worked best with a hands-on approach and he discovered he had a real aptitude for music and art.

Regarding learning disabilities, Noah, Jake, and Nigel help us to realize that no students are alike. Each child has his or her own set of weaknesses and strengths. Although the student may experience a disability in learning, it is not an intelligence disability. It does not mean the child cannot think. Children with reading challenges must problem solve their way through their work and often do so in a manner different from their peers. The ability that unique learners often develop to overcome their learning disability amazes me. In the next chapter, we will meet some patients and students who are heroes of mine. They have worked to overcome great odds and learned to become fully themselves. But first, consider the following "Strategies to Try" section on immediate solutions for reading problems.

STRATEGIES TO TRY

IF your child has difficulty reading,

THEN it is important to remember that reading ability depends on foundational skills involving the VPT systems. Exercises that promote balance incorporate the vestibular* system. Exercises that promote coordinated muscle movements incorporate the proprioceptive* system. Exercises that incorporate the sense of touch (tactile system*) also promote the necessary eye control for reading. An example of a VPT reading activity for use at home and school is as follows:

Select written text within the student's reading ability. Choose a 5- to 8-sentence paragraph.

Have the student read the paragraph out loud while using his or her "reading finger" underneath each word. Repeat reading the paragraph until it is performed error free.

Repeat reading of the paragraph without the reading finger and encourage eye tracking left to right with the eyes only and no head turning.

Once the above steps are successfully achieved, introduce clapping. Have the student clap every time he or she reads a word. Focus on steady, smooth clapping, and, therefore, steady and smooth reading out loud. Repeat until words and claps are delivered with a steady and error-free rhythm.

Physically change postures. If sitting, stand. Other changes in posture that have helped students are reading on the tummy while resting on the elbows, reading on their side while lying down, and reading in a four-point crawl position with the book placed on the floor. In addition, lying on the back underneath a table and taping the written material to the undersurface of the table so the student reads lying on his back can be quite effective. Try taping the written material to a wall and have the student read while standing on one foot. Some children might enjoy reading upside down with the head on the floor in an upside-down manner, such as you may envision an ostrich just before its head goes into the sand. This posture, in yoga terms, is known as downward facing dog.

Challenge the student to read more complex text following each of the steps above.

IF your child or student has trouble tracking their eyes to follow a sentence on a page,

THEN visual-motor* exercises can help strengthen your child's eye-tracking ability. Fun games, such as pencil mazes, finding a hidden picture, word search exercises, and tracking a single line out of a series of lines in order to find the correct end point, all incorporate visual muscle acuity. Advance to performing these exercises in a variety of different postures as well as performing the exercises while challenging your child's balance (try standing on one foot). Additional exercises that can result in improved visual abilities leading to improved reading are as follows:

Have your child closely watch a ball that they bounce and

* See Glossary for definition

ask them to count and bounce at the same time. (The timing and counting need to be perfectly matched when the ball hits the ground.) Progress counting to saying the alphabet, saying the alphabet backward, and spelling words. The ball hits the ground and the letter is spoken. Next bounce, next letter: PEPPERONI PIZZA, 14 letters, 14 perfectly executed bounces.

Other age-appropriate activities that promote normal and natural movements of the eyes are basketball, soccer, volleyball, racquet sports, such as tennis, and juggling. Martial arts activities and dance steps that require the individual to hold their vision still while the body moves are also very beneficial in enabling eye muscle movement independent of the head and neck.

While in the car, encourage your child to play "alphabet" by viewing license plate letters and the letters of road signs and buildings to identify each of the letters of the alphabet in correct sequence. With your child seated in the car and the outside world whizzing by them, this can offer an ideal method to promote eye muscle strengthening. Even specific computer games can be played, within a limited time frame, as the movement of the characters on the screen can promote eye tracking.

IF your child or student fatigues easily when reading,

THEN use activities similar to the typical development building blocks of eye strength and function. Ask your child to lie on their tummy while reading or watching television and have them support their weight through their elbows. This posture mimics an important developmental stage for eye function. Progress the posture to straight elbows/arms so that your child is weight bearing through the straight arms onto the hands. Place a therapy ball under the tummy and have them lift their legs while supporting themselves through their hands on the floor. Then raise the head up to view the television or to perform reading activities. (Perhaps place the book on floor level or on a raised surface, such as a low coffee table.)

The eye muscles' ability to move the eye independent of movement at the head and neck is a skill usually acquired in infancy and early childhood. Encouraging an infant to lie on their tummy and lift their head triggers strength not only of the neck muscles but also of the muscles that assist independent eye movements. This is particularly so when the infant learns to press up through their hands while lying on the tummy. When an infant works their muscles and manages to lift their heavy little head up by pushing through the arms, the pushing is the experience of effort that helps the brain. The tummy–lying reading exercise can help strengthen the visual system of your older child.

IF your child seems to read out loud in a choppy manner that lacks rhythm,

THEN try reading a familiar story while listening to a background rhythm such as instrumental music, a metronome, or have your child clap their hands or tap their toes while they read.

IF your child or student consistently squishes letters into

the end of the line or runs out of space while writing,

THEN they may be having difficulty judging how many words will fit on a line. They need help with their sense of space, or spatial awareness*. Until your child/student understands the amount of space their words occupy, encourage your child to utilize extra lined paper so that they can focus on displaying their knowledge of the topic versus becoming excessively distracted regarding the amount of space on the page.

CHAPTER EIGHT

HEROES AND OTHER PEOPLE WHO CHANGE THE WORLD

The classic hero who is celebrated in today's culture is the individual who has stretched the margin and extended the boundary of our thinking. Heroes open new horizons, new methods and new ways of considering old problems. Their contributions make the world more convenient, accessible, sustainable and safe.

Whether a cartoon hero, a movie hero or a modern hero in your own home or classroom, our society depends on these brave individuals to strike out and boldly go forth even when no one has traveled that path before. It becomes our journey and responsibility to embrace the unique learner; after all, their perspective might reflect answers to problems unsolvable by mainstream thinkers.

Many, many students rise to the challenge and become great because of their uniqueness. As more is understood about brain functioning, we have come to recognize individuals who have made tremendous shifts in our society. Little needs to be said regarding the profound contributions of individuals such as Winston Churchill, Leonardo da Vinci, Thomas Edison, Albert Einstein, Michelangelo, General George S. Patton, Woodrow Wilson, W.B. Yates, Bill Hewlett (cofounder HP), Nobel Peace

Prize Winner Dr. Baruj Benacerraf, and astronaut Charles "Pete" Conrad.

Despite their fame, each of these individuals was identified as learning disabled and had their own struggles. Thomas Edison was reportedly kicked out of school in the second grade because he was "too stupid to learn." If Albert Einstein went on a walk, he couldn't find his way home. The principal of his elementary school told his father, "Your son will never be a success at anything." Their teachers thought these intellectual giants couldn't learn, but the truth was that they just learned differently.

For modern day unique learners, the way is considerably better. Teachers who strive to help every child be their best are more plentiful. Parents have more tools available to understand their child and help them succeed. The outlook for these students varies depending on what yardstick is used for measurement and who is doing the measuring. Some don't believe that unique learners can and do make valuable contributions. Others believe that just having a unique learner in your life helps you be a better person and, therefore, the unique learner makes a contribution just by being. The future of these unique learners is yet unwritten. It is highly likely that the advancements of tomorrow will come from the minds of some of these individuals.

Contributing to the world doesn't have to mean inventing a new math formula, computer design or robotic engineering. Many of the unique learners I treat make heroic efforts daily in their struggle to overcome their difficulties. These efforts make them heroes in their own lives and in the lives of those around them.

A child I once worked with in my OT* practice was one of the bravest little heroes I have ever met. His name was Gabriel and I continue to stay in touch with his family. Gabriel's mother, Stacy, had a great pregnancy. She worked and played, laughed, and enjoyed her entire time being pregnant.

* See Glossary for definition

When Stacy delivered Gabriel, her first child, an unexpected event occurred. One of Gabriel's blood vessels in his brain was weak. A small brain bleed occurred and a very small portion of the damaged blood vessel wall floated through Gabriel's body and became lodged in an important artery that would normally provide oxygen and nutrients to Gabriel's right thumb. His thumb didn't grow, nor did the tips of his fingers. The small brain bleed at the time of delivery also impacted the coordination of his legs. The doctors could not tell if the stroke-like symptoms would affect his ability to learn.

Gabriel was referred to OT as an infant to progress his growth and development. Home exercises were taught to help Gabriel learn to roll despite his "sleepy" legs and to hold a toy by securing it at his midline* with both hands. Movement from one position to another was labored due to Gabriel's limited trunk rotation, a necessary function when moving the body from one position to another. Gabe's leg weakness also contributed to his trunk stiffness. As he grew up, he tended to move a bit stiffly and was lovingly referred to as Stacy's "little tin soldier."

As Gabriel entered school it became apparent that his learning style was impacted by his birth trauma. He tended to process information in a unique manner and he had a certain type of sensitivity to light and to sound. His ability to do two-handed tasks was impaired by his missing thumb and finger tips. During school, Gabriel had trouble with scissors and other desktop tasks that involved the use of his right hand.

Gabriel developed an unproductive strategy of rocking his body or swinging his legs very quickly while seated, and at times he became hard to settle down. Gabriel had difficulty stopping one thing and transitioning to the next. He would become stuck and "locked up" in his thinking. He tended to melt down when the agenda changed too quickly.

Gabriel became my first hero years ago because of his profound determination. He channeled his hypersensitivity and hyperactivity by letting off steam through movement. If noises or other irritants became too distracting, he advocated for himself to briefly leave the classroom and run an imaginary maze (an intricate game running the lines on the basketball court) in a pre-designated and safe location.

Gabriel's leg weakness was noticeable, but that did not keep him from enjoying soccer or riding a bike. He became adept at swimming and, later, water polo. Gabriel's participation in athletics on a daily basis balanced the intense stress he experienced at times when he could not leave or change his response to a loud classroom or one with many distractions.

When a little older, Gabriel gave a presentation to his middle school class on one-handed techniques. The teacher assigned a team of classmates to Gabriel and they went to other classrooms to teach other students. The principal developed a school-wide annual Sensitivity Awareness Week where booths in the gymnasium were set up. Students could experience for themselves the various common physical disabilities. A cane, an eye patch, a wheelchair, one-handed scissors, voice-activated computers, earplugs, and knee braces were made available to student participants. Students and adults alike became more understanding and accepting of uniqueness, thanks to Gabriel.

Gabriel helped his teacher and other school staff realize that through making accommodations and making "space" for the unique learner's method of problem-solving and through techniques and strategies to lessen hypersensitivities, strengthen weakness and promote a positive self-esteem, unique learners can function at a very high level. The aim for students like Gabriel is to teach him, and other unique learners, how to make these accommodations, perform these strategies, and advocate for themselves on a long-term basis. To become independent, we all need to support the unique learner to cope with their difficulties, overcome some of their challenges and to actively participate in the social human world.

Because the brain is able to alter and change a message, permanent changes in the brain's capacity to learn can occur. This is good news for unique learners. These individuals no longer need to be taught compensatory strategies that involve tricks and shortcuts. Instead they can learn through experience and, therefore, change how their brain receives messages. Once introduced to this concept, many of the unique learners I have worked with begin to see the light, which they light themselves, at the end of the tunnel.

Another beloved hero of mine is Daniel. Daniel lit his own light at the end of his tunnel and I was able to witness the positive change in his life. When I met Daniel, he was in fifth grade and struggling with school, friends, and responsibilities at home. At school, Daniel had trouble completing his work. The teacher, Daniel complained, talked too fast. He described his classmates as too noisy. Daniel's writing was characterized by his teachers as problematic and hard to read.

Writing down his homework assignments was challenging due to Daniel's poor hand coordination and his hypersensitivity to touch. Daniel was distracted by the noxious feeling of the paper sliding under his hand while he wrote. Writing a list of homework assignments added to his problems and he would put off writing the list, frequently never getting to it at all. He needed a reminder to remind himself. As you can imagine, the reminder to write the homework list was never remembered.

At home, Daniel's older brother was tired of doing Daniel's chores for him. Daniel was slow to respond to his dad's request to help pack the car for a family vacation, so Daniel's brother was solicited for the job. No problem at first, but after packing and unpacking at every hotel during their drive to visit family several states away, Daniel's brother became fed up. Daniel could not pack the luggage as quickly or efficiently as his brother. He thought his brother should do the work since he was better at it and could not see any other point of view. Daniel felt incompetent compared to his brother.

Friends came and went in Daniel's life. As a younger child, the past family photos clearly depicted Daniel as a small, adorable child throughout his elementary school years. He had ears that were just a little large for his head, huge brown eyes framed by long lashes, and a cowlick of unruly hair in the center of his forehead. He was an easy child to be with and to love.

Daniel's parents were aware of his sensitivities. He had an unexpected and odd response to food textures, clothing material, crowds of people, and loud noises. Laughter around the dinner table, family gatherings with singing birthday songs, and loud television programs were all irritating to Daniel. His parents became accustomed to leaving early, taking breaks* from parties and going for walks with Daniel, or helping him isolate with a favorite puzzle in a quiet room.

As Daniel matured, his cute small frame developed into an adolescent's physical frame. Daniel was tall. With his appearance of maturity, expectations increased. All but Daniel's immediate family members assumed that an individual of Daniel's physical stature should have a certain level of maturity and should do things a specific and mature way.

Daniel became less able to advocate for himself the more he became aware of not measuring up to others' expectations. Nothing had really changed from Daniel's perspective; he had the same sensitivities and peculiar responses to certain circumstances. Because Daniel's stature had physically matured, the world around him had changed toward him. He was no longer the big-eyed little boy that adults loved to help and support. Daniel looked like

* See Glossary for definition

a 15-year-old adolescent and was expected to act accordingly. Daniel could have responded with a "No fair, no fair!" attitude. He did not. Daniel was a hero about it.

With collaboration between knowledgeable school staff and therapists, Daniel focused on an intelligent inquiry toward his sensitivities and his problems. He continued to be highly distracted by a noisy classroom, frustrated by his effortful handwriting, and sensitive to all kinds of textures. One day he had to go home at lunch and change his clothes due to the feel of his new pants.

Despite these difficulties, or perhaps because of them, Daniel developed a curiosity toward himself. Like a scientist, he tried to change the variables to see if he could reduce his distractibility at school. He became his own living science experiment. He became his own non-judgmental observer*.

Many times Daniel's ideas were met with success. He realized that his problem with writing related to an intolerance to the feel of the paper sliding under his hand. Daniel tried a variety of clear plastic sheet protector materials cut to the size of his hand in order to prevent the noxious feeling of rubbing his hand against the paper. The plastic sheet was placed between his hand and the paper. The plastic material slid along the paper so that Daniel's hand didn't have to.

Daniel's supportive family members provided him with a sense of humor toward himself and compassion toward others. His family helped him to feel safe and secure while he tried out new behaviors. Gradually, he developed compassion even toward himself and his predicament.

Daniel's high school teachers noticed a change. Assignments were complete and handed in, homework lists prepared, and improved coping within the classroom was noticed. Daniel's self-esteem was bolstered by the teachers' positive remarks. He became an advocate for himself and calmly asserted his preferred

* See Glossary for definition

coping strategy for dealing with noisy and stressful classroom environments. Daniel discovered that drawing helped him listen. Many of his teachers supported Daniel in allowing him to perform simple and repetitious artwork during class to take his mind off the frustration of noisy peers. The teachers understood that this would be a legitimate strategy and they refrained from assuming that he was not listening or that he was goofing around.

At present, Daniel is fielding opportunities from a variety of commercial artists within the cartoon industry to become a professional artist. Not bad for a high school kid! He is also appreciated for his compassion toward people and all living things. His artwork depicts this compassion through the details and complexity of the animals and creatures he creates. The intricacies of his drawings and his caricatures represent people in his life and suggest that he has a profound understanding of all that is occurring around him.

When the world thought that Daniel was disengaged, disingenuous, and disregarding of others, he was highly present and highly aware. Daniel had always been sensitive to his surroundings. In fact, he demonstrated an unusual ability to discern the underlying emotions in the people around him. When I first met Daniel in fifth grade he was grappling with psychological issues that seemed far too sophisticated for his age. As a high school student, his thinking had expand to world problems such as animal conservation and the problem of deforestation. Daniel is a hero because he has embraced who he really is in order to become the accomplished young man that he is today.

Sometimes I become aware of heroes long after I have discharged them from OT. Past patients and I see one another in the community and it gives us a chance to catch up. One day when I was buying flowers, the florist told me that her son used to receive OT services with me as a young child. Her son, Kevin, recently finished high school and was attending college. Higher education was a great accomplishment for him, she explained, given his shaky start to school life.

When I worked with Kevin he was in preschool. I saw him in my clinic off and on for two years to help him with his unusual sensory responses to the world around him. When I checked through my past treatment notes, I recalled that when he was a young child he had many difficulties. Kevin couldn't relate to his peers because he had trouble turn taking and sharing with classmates. He didn't enjoy the usual toys and games that other children enjoyed. Loud sounds, bright lights, certain smells, and many kinds of foods were intolerable. In school, he had a very hard time following the class structure.

It was wonderful to hear of Kevin's progress. While I selected my flowers, Kevin's mother gave me a detailed update. While he was in high school, Kevin developed an interest in science. When he was accepted by a nearby college, he took an interest in biology. Kevin presently lives on campus and will work in the summer for the Forestry Department. Kevin's mother described his friends that she had met and his teachers she had spoken with. She was amazed at her heroic son having worked through his sensory difficulties and having achieved so much in his life. Before another customer came into the florist's shop, we were both wiping tears from our eyes. I had goose bumps for hours after our conversation. I am so proud of Kevin.

On another occasion, a parent called our facility to schedule an appointment for her son to evaluate and treat his headache pain. She told our receptionist that I had worked with her son, Anthony, many years ago.

Anthony and his mother came into our clinic and it was a happy reunion. After a little reminiscing, we talked together in a private treatment room about his headaches. I was overwhelmed by how tall and mature this senior high school student appeared.

His manner of speaking, his self-awareness, and his keen interest in life were mesmerizing. Anthony was one of those high school kids who you really want to be with.

Anthony and his mother told me of his musical accomplishments. Recently, he had traveled to Chicago with his school band. He was an honors band student and his love was jazz. My husband used to manage a jazz lounge, so Anthony and I had lots in common reminiscing about the great jazz legends and the newer musicians while we worked on his posture, breathing pattern, and upper body strength to reduce headache pain. We even reinitiated some of the old sensory integration* strategies from years ago to reawaken previous techniques for exerting control on triggers that tended to cause headaches.

The old treatment notes on Anthony refreshed my memory of his past difficulties with attention span and changes in routine. Family members, friends, and teachers were confounded by his unexpected response to events that others seemed to easily deal with. Life seemed hard and abrasive to Anthony many years ago. Through all of these challenges, Anthony was the kindest and sweetest young person you could ever meet. I remember his great hugs during our treatment sessions. Over time, his sensitivities became more manageable. Anthony's friends and grades took on greater meaning in his life. His love for music was obvious.

Anthony has become another one of my heroes. He has achieved academic success and impressive musical achievements. He has a very bright future. I feel tempted to get his autograph right now as he is destined for musical greatness! And he still has a great hug.

Parents of unique learners are also heroes. I have met hundreds of parents in the course of my work with unique learners. Many of these people have amazed me with their love and dedication toward their children. Unique learners are affected in different ways and to different levels of severity. Regardless of how involved their child's difficulties are, these parents must balance their own hopes and dreams for what they wish their child could become.

When a child is born, parents are filled with aspirations for their future athlete, artist, scholar and ballerina. Typical children may have to bear the weight of their parents' expectations, but a unique learner cannot. It is the parent who must change their expectations to match the particular strengths and weaknesses of their child.

These parents are heroes because they understand that their best role is not a role that tries to change their unique learner child. One parent told me, "The important thing to keep in mind is that you aren't looking for mastery in these activities. Rather, you are looking for that 'brain working here*' behavior."

Parents tell me that they can see how hard their child is working to meet the demands of the task. They imagine the cogs turning in the student's mind to problem-solve and to learn from past mistakes and past experiences. When you see this evidence, make space for "brain working here" magic to occur. When a child shows this degree of motivation, positive progress is just around the corner.

For a parent, letting go of an assumed lifestyle and the wishful thinking that accompanies it can be painful at first. The parent heroes who come to embrace their unique learner's potential also learn to do the same thing for their typical learners, for themselves and for all people in their lives. These parents are changed forever by the gifts and attributes of their unique learner. These are homes where all children thrive and adults do too.

Teachers are definitely heroes. Zachary helped his teacher to become amazing. Years ago, he was the first student with autism spectrum disorder (ASD)* who had enrolled at the school. His teacher quickly identified Zachary's unique needs and collaborated with the gym teacher. She embedded movement breaks* into the structured curriculum well before movement during seated class work was recognized as valuable. The adept gym teacher could see that, even in the population of more typical students, certain movements helped some students and not others.

The classroom-friendly exercises were individualized for each student and changed over time. Despite the young age of this first-grade classroom of students, the teacher was amazed at how quickly they settled into their desk work. Their understanding of the classroom structure and their independence in learning was intact by the third month of school. These goals of learning are not usually seen until the sixth or seventh month of a first-grade school year.

Because of Zachary and his conscientious, caring teacher, the outcomes for an entire class of first-grade students improved. Thank you, teacher; you are a hero!

I am working with a hero at the time of writing this book. Her name is Henny*. If you don't known Henny, you should. She is amazing. Henny contacted me to assist her with a research project on promoting fine motor skills* for her piano students with autism spectrum disorder. I drove four hours and sat in her apartment watching her teach all afternoon. Henny teaches piano to students around the world using Skype.

While I was in her Oakland, California, one-bedroom, she taught students in England, France, Canada, and the United States. Each of these students was profoundly impacted by symptoms of autism. They tended to be nonverbal, had limited sitting tolerance and limited attention span. Odd mannerisms such as rocking back and forth while sitting and prolonged hand flapping interrupted the piano playing up to 50 percent of the 30-minute lesson. At first naive glance, it seemed amazing to me that anything got accomplished.

Henny kept a steady pace with her students and worked through the pages of the piano books. I watched her students play individual notes, then chords, and then play notes and chords with both hands. Her students were playing real and recognizable music. They were sight reading the musical notes, isolating each finger to play a chord blending piano chords with both hands, and maintaining the timing and rhythm sufficient to recognize the music piece. Some of the parents reported that these skills translated to use of a computer keyboard.

As the afternoon with Henny proceeded, she showed me that the furtive glances of her students who tended to quickly look at their piano books through the periphery of their vision was all that was needed for them to read the notes. I didn't think they were looking at the musical notes at all until Henny pointed this out. She said that her students could visually memorize the entire line of notes with just a quick glance. Henny said most of her students had a photographic memory.

Where I saw nonsensical and nonproductive hand flapping, she saw a student practicing muscle memory with their fingers. I began to see that the hand flapping wasn't just a stereotypical behavior characteristic of ASD, but a method for the fingers to practice moving in a sequence required in the new piano lesson. It wasn't just random wrist and finger flapping; it was the C finger, D finger, and E finger practicing their routine. The same finger movements on the piano resulted in the notes being played correctly.

When the student rocked their body, it was the rhythm of the musical piece that they were taking in. When I thought they were just rocking (because sometimes individuals with ASD just rock back and forth), later in the lesson it became clear that the rhythm of the body rocking blended with the rhythm of the musical piece.

How did Henny know this? Henny is a graduate student with autism spectrum disorder. She described a very troubled life as a young person until she embraced her uniqueness. Earlier in her life she was at the mercy of well-meaning adults trying to change and fix her. Henny began to realize that her way of learning was different from those around her.

Henny loves her quirky world. She's content with the quirky things she eats and the times that she eats, her quirky way of resting and her odd sleeping hours. She has a tactile mat underneath her keyboard for sensory input to her feet that tend to kick and sway while playing the piano. Her cozy apartment and relationship with her compassionate landlord and local neighbors and friends have all provided Henny with a sense of emotional comfort. She has a fierce desire to help others on the autism spectrum embrace their own uniqueness and succeed in their own lives. Her graduate work is based on this premise. Henny is a hero and she is developing heroes all around the world. (For those readers interested in Henny's work, please see the Glossary section under Henny*.)

These heroes help us to realize, again and again, the powerful contributions that we are all capable of making to help our community and our society. Unique learners, when supported to use their strengths, can contemplate problems and resolve issues from a different perspective than mainstream thinkers. That difference could be the key to their success.

Over decades of experience as an occupational and physical therapist*, I have seen countless unique learners improve their ability to function in the world. Of course, there are difficulties and sometimes even hardship with sadness. When the characteristics and personality traits that could really help a unique learner are not allowed full expression, the individual never feels safe and secure enough to explore their own unique and varied responses to the world. Often these children and adults feel compelled to hide their idiosyncrasies from others. They become adept at deflecting problems onto external sources. Complaining, blaming, and externalizing their problems cause others to feel a similar uneasiness. The unique learner may feel an exaggerated sense of victimization and when these problems go unrecognized, social isolation and self-inflicted negative behavior* can follow. It is imperative to reach these individuals before further tragedy has an opportunity for irreversible damage. The students and individuals we have met in the previous chapters are all heroes and have worked to overcome profound difficulties.

Your unique learner knows compassion and humility better than most students. Children with learning disabilities learn humility and how to get along with others. Most approach problems differently. They do not always organize their approach to chores and homework like other children. They do not always move predictably, one step at a time. They think in whole pictures. Many times, these students will see a solution to something and develop a plan differently and more quickly than other people. Different can be better, in the working world. Unique learners may be at an advantage as they mature, as they take in information in their own way and can reach different and better solutions.

The potential for change offered by the unique learner is, perhaps, the greatest contribution that this population of individuals can make to our human society. We must embrace the hero and, in so doing, we embrace ourselves. The knowledge that the reader acquires by considering the needs of a unique learner can change them forever. So, in this manner, each reader is also a hero.

GLOSSARY

Academic-related occupational therapy (OT) – A licensed occupational therapist* will function in the school system to ensure students have access to their individualized curriculum. The OT's aim is to support positive learning behaviors in a classroom-based setting and to encourage sustained participation in all academic tasks. Fine motor skills, attention to task (often through sensory strategies), and sequencing for reasoning skills are all areas OT can help.

Adaptive physical education teacher – A physical education teacher who is trained in the methods of helping students with developmental delays improve their gross motor, fine motor, balance, and endurance as they relate to age-appropriate exercise, school experiences and campus safety.

Asperger's – Asperger's disorder is a learning disability that affects social communication, organizational abilities and acquiring knowledge. Asperger's is considered to be on the autism spectrum.

Attention deficit hyperactivity disorder (ADHD) – ADHD is characterized by a pattern of behaviors presenting in multiple settings that include difficulty organizing, excessive talking, failure to pay close attention to details, inability to remain seated, and fidgeting. Impulsivity is also noted with difficulty awaiting turns. Often interrupting and blurting out the answer before the question has been completed is an observation made by many teachers.

Auditory sensitivity – An increase in the awareness of sounds of all types, such as loud noises, sudden noises, and a continuous sound like the background buzz of a busy classroom. This increased awareness can range from a mild startle to physical pain.

Autism/autism spectrum disorder (ASD) – Autism is a disorder that has a huge range of characteristics. Doctors will sometimes refer to individuals as "on the spectrum." The doctors mean that the child has behaviors that fall within a cluster of problems. Children on the autism spectrum may have difficulty relating to people and things. They may have difficulty communicating and their ability to process sensations and to perceive and understand events can be dysfunctional. People with ASD may develop at a different rate. Their physical and cognitive growth may be skewed and they may have difficulty moving in a balanced, functional, and typical fashion.

Brain working here – A detective/observer is looking for evidence that says, "Brain working here!" Certain behaviors and actions promote children in their ultimate job of learning how to learn. The adult should foster independent problem-solving and try to create a general sense of curiosity in their children and students. Brain working here behavior allows children to use their brain to their greatest capacity.

Break – Many unique learners need a (brain-refreshing) classroom break in order to refocus. The break can be performed in the classroom or outside of the classroom. Breaks can be determined by the student's behavior or they can be pre-designated. If a child can attend to an activity at home or in the classroom for only

30-40 minutes before a meltdown, then set a pre-designated break roughly every 30 minutes.

In-class breaks can consist of activities that do not interrupt other students, such as desktop fidgets, doodling, or enjoyable exercises while seated. When outside of classroom breaks are necessary, the child should be taken to an environment where it is safe for them to move their body in a variety of ways, such as walking, running, jumping, rolling, and even utilizing a swing set. Although these activities seem very playful and are used as a reward for the general school population, unique learners require these very actions in order to reboot their brains and refocus on classroom material.

Brushing program – An OT may recommend a brushing program. It is a program that aims to improve the sense of touch and the sense of pressure. An improved sense of touch is needed for printing and improved touch/pressure helps by calming. Brushing with a standard scrub brush provides a balancing state to the brain. It involves stroking the brush along the surface of the skin in the same direction the hair grows. The softness or hardness of the brush can be varied to help desensitize the tactile system (skin). At school, the brushing motion occurs on the arms and wrists. The brushing can be performed over clothing. This sensory program is best provided at regular intervals.

Chaos/chaotic – Some behaviors lead to more confusing and negative circumstances. The triggers for the child's confusion and poor behavior (chaos) need to be noted and kept to a minimum whenever possible. Because the unique learner demonstrates both coherent and chaotic behaviors, the observer-detective also needs to watch for those things that appropriately focus the child's attention, leading to mental coherence.

Chewy – Some unique learners have not fully matured beyond the oral-motor* stage and continue to developmentally require items in their mouths, whether edible or not. The OT strategy is twofold: to work on developing the sense of touch through the fingertips so that the unique learner becomes less reliant on the mouth; and, at the same time, designate items that can be provided for the child to put in their mouth (until they begin to use their sense of touch in their fingertips more than their mouth to make sense of the world). Edible foods that offer resistance when biting, such as carrots, apples, and fruit rollups, are excellent. Commercially purchased nontoxic "chewies" can also be obtained. For example, a pencil topper is a nontoxic device placed on top of a pencil as a type of "chewy" for the unique learner to bite on.

Coherence/coherent – Behaviors that serve to organize performance in a logical manner. A coherent mindset is required for learning readiness.

Crossing the midline – The midline is an imaginary line that vertically divides the body into two halves. Because the right side of the brain controls the left side of the body, and vice versa, crossing the midline can stimulate the two hemispheres of the brain to function together. An example of crossing the midline is when the left hand reaches across (the midline) to the right side of the body to pick something up.

Detective/detective mode/observer/nonjudgmental observer – Observing unique learners requires suspending any judgments or assumptions regarding their behaviors. Using this detective approach, the observer watches and learns before judging and criticizing. To become a nonjudgmental observer/detective, you must presuppose three important facts:

One: The unique learner is already equipped with the necessary sensory-motor abilities to be successful in adapting to the world around them.

Two: An innate drive exists in all of us leading to desirable, organized social behavior.

Three: Patterns are apparent in which behaviors and events either contribute to organized and coherent actions or they contribute to nonproductive incoherent or chaotic actions.

Differentiate/differentiation – The ability to distinguish between two separate things. Eye muscles need to move independently of neck muscles. This enables a person to follow an object or a line of print using just their eyes and not moving their head. Differentiation is also needed when printing because the finger muscles need to move while the wrist stays still. For efficient printing, the eyes must be differentiated from the head and neck, and the fingers must be differentiated from the wrist.

Dynamic moving muscles/dynamic muscle control – Muscles hold still, move, and they work in concert with other body parts. When the muscle works to hold the joint still, it is a static contraction. When the muscle works to allow controlled movement, it is a dynamic contraction. You lift a bucket of water off the floor with dynamic (moving) muscles and hold the pail still with your elbow slightly bent and locked, by static (holding) muscles.

Dyslexia – A condition that results in difficulty reading, sometimes in isolation of any other learning problem.

Elope, elopement – Elope or elopement is a term used by school personnel to describe a student who runs away. The student may move to the opposite side of the playground when the bell rings, but with encouragement, the child reaches their classroom on time.

Facilitated state – An excited state in which students or adults have difficulty paying attention and difficulty sitting still. The OT aim with these individuals would be to shift their excessively excited state to a more balanced and middle-of-the-road mode through inhibitory* strategies.

Facilitatory/facilitatory signals – The brain sends out messages that transmit signals causing the body to respond. These signals are called facilitatory when they stimulate (or excite) the nervous system and cause either an appropriate alert response or, in the case of hyperactivity, a less-desirable fast and chaotic (dysfunctional) behavior.

Fidgets – Fidgeting with a small toy or other item in the hand can improve a unique learner's ability to listen. A small portion of resistive putty can be considered a working toy and is used by unique learners in order to apply their brain to the task at hand. These items must not be considered toys. It is offered as a strategy to stay focused and never offered as a reward or removed as a punishment. Fidgets are usually small devices that do not interrupt other students during classroom lessons. The stimulation through the tactile senses helps to modulate and improve learning readiness. By using a fidget or some quiet desktop manipulative object, unique learners will be able to organize their brains and perform without the negative effect on others (excessive wiggling or excessive talking).

Fidgets that I refer to as "working toys" should be age-appropriate and small. A palm-sized finger exercise device that is designed for guitar players can be an excellent fidget for a high school or college-age student. Adults seem to do best with items that fit in their pocket, such as a single marble. Younger children may enjoy an animal-shaped small squish device. The device must have appeal to the user but not be so enjoyable that other students become distracted from their own work.

Fight or flight stress reaction – The fight or flight stress reaction can occur suddenly when an individual feels threatened. A change in blood flow occurs. The body prepares itself, both mentally and physically, to either fight and defend their position or run away from the danger. Once the situation is resolved, the blood flow returns to its normal resting level.

Fine motor/fine motor skills/fine motor control – The integrity and balance of the small muscles and joints of the hand work together to achieve refined finger movements and precision in grasp and release. The typical preschool child utilizes their fine motor skills for drawing and, eventually, for use of scissors. Early childhood is an important time for learning fine motor skills. Developmental milestones such as dexterity, bilateral coordination, and eye/hand coordination are acquired in early childhood.

A functional grasp of the pencil begins to develop at 5 years of age with the pencil held in the tips of the thumb and neighboring two fingers. The movement of the pencil is powered through the fingers. Drawing skills progress in the following sequence: vertical line (2 years), horizontal line (3 years), cross (4 years), and diagonal line (5 years). A development of scissor skills follows other tool use. Mature use of scissors is not achieved until 5-6 years of age because it requires isolated finger use.

Gross motor – The body is made of large and small muscles with large and small joints. The knee and hip are large joints with large muscles: the quadriceps and the hamstring. The finger joints are small and have very small muscles. Gross motor movement is performed by larger joints and muscles. Fine motor movement is performed by the small joints and muscles in the hand. As outlined in this book, gross motor is needed for fine motor development and fine motor development is needed to mature gross motor skills.

Henny – For more information on Henny's research, visit her website: https://hennyk.com

Hyper – Hyper is a root word that has the meaning of being over or above normal. It is used this way in many words and typically when used with another word should be taken as this root meaning. Hyper is also used to describe someone who is hyperactive.

Hyperactive – Unusually or extremely energetic, typically referring to constant activity and sometimes disruptive behavior

Individuating – Typically developing children can distinguish themselves from their environment at around two years of age. They separate their sense of self from their sense of the environment around them. Unique learners don't always mature through this stage in the same way. For example, unique learners may consider everything in their field of vision as belonging to themselves. They will grasp at people and objects, not understanding that they are separate.

Inhibitory/inhibitory signals/inhibitory strategies – Inhibitory strategies are actions that calm the brain and nerves from working too quickly. Inhibitory strategies could consist of using a soft voice, low lights, warm room temperature, and tight swaddling of your infant in a blanket to settle down, slow down, and help fall asleep. When it comes to inhibitory strategies, there can be an appropriate calm-down and slow-down response and there can also be an inappropriate, excessive shutdown response.

Learning challenges – The word "challenge" implies that it is a matter of opinion whether or not a problem in learning exists. A learning challenge is a learning style that falls outside of what might be expected in a typical classroom. When students think in a whole-picture fashion, it is difficult to learn from someone who thinks in smaller, sequential steps. While in school, learning-challenged students often require assistance from adults who place an emphasis on individualized learning. In many cases, the learning challenge can be a problem while a student is in school but an asset later in life.

Learning disability – Learning disability is the common term used for those who have difficulty acquiring knowledge and skills to the same level and in the same manner as other students their same age. It does not indicate low intelligence. It is my experience (over thirty years of treating unique learners) that those given this label are really not unable to learn; they simply learn differently from more mainstream learners.

Learning readiness behaviors – Learning readiness behaviors are student actions that help the student best process new information, new experiences and retain what was learned. Sitting in their seats, looking forward, listening to the teacher, and staying focused on the task at hand are examples of positive learning readiness behaviors in elementary and middle school-aged students.

Midline – The midline is an imaginary line that vertically divides the body into two halves. Because the right side of the brain controls the left side of the body, and vice versa, crossing the midline can stimulate the two hemispheres of the brain to function together. An example of crossing the midline is when the left hand reaches across (the midline) to the right side of the body to pick something up.

Modulate/regulate/self-regulate – Self-regulation is the life skill of independently managing one's own moods, behaviors, and actions. Good self-regulation is an optimal mode for living in our complex world. Poor self-regulation, sometimes called dysregulation, leads to a less productive and more chaotic approach to the world. The concept of self-regulation has recently become a new awareness for teachers and parents who are trying to help unique learners.

The occupational therapy goal in a school setting is always to help the student modulate their brain's level of arousal in order to achieve the best outcome possible for that particular circumstance. To regulate requires maintaining the correct mood/mode to participate for as long as other students do.

To assist a child or student to better regulate (or modulate) their erratic behavior, the adult can employ strategies suggested throughout this book. For example, a brushing program can be initiated by the adult. The child is gradually encouraged to perform parts of the regimen independently in order to develop self-regulation with less dependence on external sources for their sense of calmness and well-being.

Motor cortex – Part of the brain in charge of voluntary movement.

Motor system/sensory-motor system – The motor system sends the outgoing messages that direct the muscles to integrate with the joints to perform correct and well-planned actions. The motor portion of the sensory-motor system has a different function than the sensory portion. The motor system allows us to react. The sensory system allows us to perceive. You sense something with your sensory system and you react to it through your motor system.

Movement breaks – Students frequently do very well in a busy classroom environment when offered movement breaks on a regular basis. Moving the body helps activate the brain and promotes improved attention span. Younger students need more frequent breaks than older students, but all students respond favorably to an education model that supports movement and activity. PE and recess are not rewards; they are a vital part of the curriculum.

Multisensory learning – Multisensory learning is based on the premise that a healthy brain involves proper integration of the entire sensory system. Touch, taste, smell, sight, hearing, and perception of movement through the vestibular and proprioceptive systems comprise the entire human sensory system. Children, and especially children who are unique learners, need to learn how to use their brains more effectively and more easily. Children have a developmental need to learn. Learning to organize their brain will help a child's brain work better.

Neuroanatomy – The study of the human anatomy and its nervous system.

Neurophysiology/neurophysiologic – The study of the functioning of the nervous system.

Neuroplasticity – The fundamental property of the brain to adapt is known as neuroplasticity. The nerve cells, or neurons, are changeable (or plastic) in their character. The brain is always learning how to learn. It creates new pathways and augments older pathways.

We can navigate through a forest more efficiently through the traveled path. We will continue to use that path until a fallen tree or other obstacle causes us to change direction and then we seek an alternative route to reach the same destination. The brain works in a similar way and, with repetition, will find an alternative pathway to accomplish the same task.

If certain parts of the brain fail to operate optimally, then other parts can take over. The brain is constantly adapting itself. The brain's property of adaptation allows for greater creativity and receptiveness to learning, even into adulthood. Adaptation is a fundamental function of neuroplasticity.

Observer/nonjudgmental observer – See detective/detective mode.

Occupational therapist – A licensed individual whose occupation is based on creating a plan to help an individual with developmental challenges, physical injury or illness, cognitive impairment, or a dysfunctional condition (such as psychosocial, mental or educational), in order that they become successful and independent in their setting.

OT treatment is aimed to promote independence in life skills. It is initiated with an OT evaluation. When evaluating a unique learner, the following considerations are important:

Is the behavior universal or are they showing difficulties only at certain and specific times?

Does their level of stimulation seem appropriate most of the time or are there times when they seem inappropriately revved up or too slowed down?

How is their sense of rhythm? Can they keep time to a clapping or stomping beat?

How is their coordination overall? Do they often appear to be awkward and clumsy or are they smooth, timely, and organized?

Occupational therapy (OT) – A form of medical and school-based intervention that utilizes purposeful activity to achieve functional outcomes.

Oral-motor – The physical movement of the oral system is accomplished by muscles of the lips, jaw, tongue, and larynx.

Over-stimulated behavior/over-stimulation – Beyond excitement, this hyper-excited student is wound-up! It is important to determine what may trigger wound-up nonproductive behavior. Some unique learners seem like puppies in that they can become overly flighty when adults approach them too quickly, use intense eye contact or emit excessive sounds and vocalizations.

Immediately after any over-stimulating event (and for a considerable time following the event), be aware of subtle changes in your unique learner's behavior. Changes in eating patterns, social responses to friends and family members, as well as a change in sleeping pattern are all noteworthy. As a detective/observer, you must note the manner in which the over-stimulating event either provided shut-down behavior, moved the student toward an alert and calm learning ready state, or caused a cascade of poor behavior.

Perception – The ability to organize sensory information into meaningful patterns.

Physical therapist – A licensed individual whose occupation is based on creating a plan to help an individual recover from injury, surgery, or other pathology that reduces their physical level of function. When physical therapists work with school children, it is to ensure there are no architectural barriers and that all students enjoy safety on the campus.

Physical therapy – A form of therapy for the preservation, enhancement, or restoration of movement and physical function that may be compromised due to disease, injury, or disability.

Position in space – If you move your arm, you become aware of your arm's position as it moves at the side of your body. You are aware of your arm's position in space. You can also have awareness of your physical surroundings and know the position in space of your pet dog so that you don't trip. Position in space is a complex sensory experience that requires a well-functioning VPT.

Positive learning behaviors – When a student is able to attend to the teacher and demonstrate an interest in learning, teachers refer to this quality as positive learning behaviors. When interviewing teachers on this topic, they state that students will lean forward, maintain their shoulders facing forward toward the teacher, eye contact, head nodding, and volunteering answers. Teachers are also aware of students' positive learning behaviors through their work performance. They know that each student is different in their ability to look and listen to their teacher. Classrooms, today, have students up and down and moving around, throughout the teacher's lesson.

Postural support muscles – Muscles that are close to the spine help support the body in an upright position. In addition, the muscles around the hips and low back as well as the shoulder and neck contribute to an upright sitting or standing posture. Collectively, these muscles are referred to as the postural support muscles.

Proprioceptive system – The proprioceptive system allows us to detect the movement and actions of our joints through an internal sensory mechanism. Tiny receptors exist inside the joints and muscles that detect any slight movement. This important information is immediately sent to the brain where it makes sure we are moving our body correctly.

Regulate/self-regulate/modulate – Self-regulation is the life skill of independently managing one's own moods, behaviors, and actions. Good self-regulation is an optimal mode for living in our complex world. Poor self-regulation, sometimes called dysregulation, leads to a less productive and more chaotic approach to the world. The concept of self-regulation has recently become a new awareness for teachers and parents who are trying to help unique learners.

The occupational therapy goal in a school setting is always to help the student modulate their brain's level of arousal in order to achieve the best outcome possible for that particular circumstance. To regulate requires maintaining the correct mood/mode to participate for as long as other students do.

To assist a child or student to better regulate (or modulate) their erratic behavior, the adult can employ strategies suggested throughout this book. For example, a brushing program can be initiated by the adult. The child is gradually encouraged to perform parts of the regimen independently in order to develop self-regulation with less dependence on external sources for their sense of calmness and well-being.

Right brain/left brain learning – Unique learners benefit from activities that promote the integration of the right and left hemispheres of the brain. Generally, these activities involve use of the large muscles with an emphasis on timing and rhythm as well as an essential component of crossing the midline with the extremity. Activities that promote right brain/left brain processing and crossing the midline can stimulate the two hemispheres of the brain to function together. An example activity would be the "patty-cake" type of hand game.

Role playing – Role playing can be employed in order to help unique learners learn how to interact with others. Students can discover that they have a choice to engage in another person's anger and perpetuate a trigger of their own negative thinking, or to stay calm and express compassion. Staying calm prevents the chemical burst of anger in their own body.

Self-inflicted negative behavior – To disregard this vital population can be life threatening. Anxiety disorders, compulsive behaviors, and social withdrawal may be future consequences for the untreated unique learner. Individuals who are misunderstood by those around them may even engage in antisocial behaviors and suicide attempts. Healthy behavior requires a range of responses to events and requires the emotional security to try out new solutions.

Self-regulate/regulate/modulate – Self-regulation is the life skill of independently managing one's own moods, behaviors, and actions. Good self-regulation is an optimal mode for living in our complex world. Poor self-regulation, sometimes called dysregulation, leads to a less productive and a more chaotic approach to the world. The concept of self-regulation has recently become a new awareness for teachers and parents who are trying to help unique learners.

The occupational therapy goal in a school setting is always to help the student modulate their brain's level of arousal in order to achieve the best outcome possible for that particular circumstance. To regulate requires maintaining the correct mood/mode to participate for as long as other students do.

To assist a child or student to better regulate (or modulate) their erratic behavior, the adult can employ strategies suggested throughout this book. For example, a brushing program can be initiated by the adult. The child is gradually encouraged to perform parts of the regimen independently in order to develop self-regulation with less dependence on external sources for their sense of calmness and well-being.

Sensory integration – Sensory integration occurs when the brain receives messages from the senses via the nervous system and turns them into appropriate motor and behavioral responses. When this integration does not occur properly, the person may have difficulty with coordination and learning and may demonstrate unexpected behavior.

Sensory integration disorder – The word "disorder" suggests a condition that may be reversible. A sensory integration disorder describes an individual whose ability to process sensory information is atypical and causes difficulty in dealing with day-to-day circumstances.

Sensory-motor system – The sensory-motor system is a specialized system that allows an individual to perceive the world around them and to respond to that world in a functional manner. The sensory portion of the sensory-motor system has a different function than the motor portion. The sensory system allows us to perceive. The motor system allows us to react. You sense something through your sensory system and you react to it through your motor system.

Sensory system/sensory processing/sensory processing system – The sensory system consists of taste, touch, smell, sight, hearing, vestibular, and proprioceptive information. This sensory information can come from the internal or the external environment. The information is registered by the entire sensory processing system: the brain, nerves and organs. The brain integrates the sensory information and relays it to various body systems in order to organize a response.

Spatial awareness – Spatial awareness allows for correct depth perception as well as the ability to determine the space between one object in relationship to another. This perceptual ability is important in understanding directional language concepts, such as in, out, up, down, in front of, behind, between, left, and right. It provides awareness as to how far away something is so that we can keep track of where we are and avoid obstacles.

Squeezes (body squeezes) – Squeezes are performed on the arms and legs of unique learners by the adult partner using both of their hands to squeeze the child's extremity along its entire length. The squeeze is about the same pressure that you might use to squeeze water from a large sponge with both hands. Compressions around the trunk can be performed with a softly cupped hand pressing down with about the same pressure you would use to press the water from a sponge sitting on the counter. Head hugs are squeezes performed by placing one hand on either side of the unique learner's head and applying a gentle compression. These co-contractions are very calming for the brain of a unique learner. Frequently the student will extend their arm, seeking out squeezes in a nonverbal fashion. The use of a weighted blanket or other weighted objects can simulate squeezes and be performed independently.

Stimulate/stimulation – Stimulation results in raised or excited levels of physiological or nerve activity in the body. Overstimulation refers to taking this stimulation too far and overloading the physiologic systems.

Tactile hypersensitivity – A problem of increased sensitivity to touch, textures, pressure and/or temperature level. Sometimes it can interrupt healthy functioning.

Tactile system – Our sense of touch is managed by our tactile system. Touch allows for our ability to process pressure sensitivity as well as temperature sensitivity. Until we mature our tactile awareness in early childhood, we will continue to rely on more basic exploration through the mouth.

Task completion behavior – Understanding the instructions, initiating the project, actively participating and completing the project within the specified time frame are all qualities of task completion behavior. Some of us require assistance initiating tasks and others with finishing them. Task completion behavior implies independence from start to finish.

Therapy ball – A therapy ball (or exercise ball) is readily available commercially. In OT, we use the appropriately sized ball as a "round chair" and not a toy. Children and adults who sit on the round chair immediately notice that their posture improves. The round, dynamic, rolling surface continually offers data to the brain regarding how gravity is operating on their body and what muscles they need to activate on a moment-by-moment basis. Although it sounds like a lot of work, people generally feel more comfortable using the round chair than a standard chair. Therapy balls are becoming office solutions for adults, too.

Unstructured/structured playground time – Often, the structure of the classroom environment is far less anxiety provoking for unique learners than surviving the unstructured playground time during recess. The lack of structure during these breaks from classroom can be bewildering for many unique learners. Unique learners tend to flourish when consistent structure is provided whereby they can anticipate the activities that comprise their day. An adult may need to help them structure their time at recess.

Vestibular system (V) – The vestibular system allows us to feel gravity. The vestibular system keeps us upright and prevents us from falling. It is comprised of the vestibular organs and all of their connections throughout the body.

Visual-motor/visual-motor tracking – Visual-motor tracking is the method in which the small eye muscles coordinate together in order to view a target. The target can be either still or moving.

Effortless reading requires that the eyes move together but independent from the head and neck.

Visual-spatial awareness – Visual-spatial awareness describes the ability to look at an object in relationship to another object. To be able to accurately reach an item on your desk, you must be able to judge the distance within the space between that item and your coffee mug. Poor visual spatial awareness would result in knocking over your coffee mug.

VPT/VPT systems/VPT sensory systems/VPT sensory facilitation – The vestibular (V), proprioceptive (P), and tactile (T) systems provide an overall balanced state to the entire brain and body. The vestibular and proprioceptive systems are involved in coordinating and balancing physical movement. The tactile system provides us with our sense of touch and it is also a pathway that provides us with emotional calmness. It is important to realize that the sensory system integrates vestibular information (regarding our sense of balance), proprioceptive information (regarding our ability to move), and tactile information (touching and feeling) to help ready the brain for learning. When the VPT sensory processing systems are working well, there is continual activation of the visual and auditory pathways. Students can look and listen better when their VPT systems are functioning well. Even athletes use these techniques to promote better performance.

Wait it out – Unique learners need to develop the skill of waiting it out when they become frustrated. Although triggers for frustration seem to happen automatically for many unique learners, they need to learn to wait it out. Most negative thought patterns, anger for instance, trigger a cascade of chemical releases that surge through the brain and body. Recognizing the experience to be biochemical and short term in nature, the feeling can dissipate within seconds.

Weighted blanket – It can be a calming strategy for an overly active or anxious child or adult. The weighted blanket is placed over an individual to snuggle underneath and serves to calm the nervous system. It is a commercially available product or an item that can be made from a standard blanket that has pockets throughout for bean-bag like weights to be evenly distributed.

Wheelbarrow relays – This makes a fun game and is helpful on several levels for the unique learner. A wheelbarrow is performed by having the child lie flat on his or her stomach on the floor with their palms down, elbows bent. Then a trustworthy helper grasps the child's ankles, lifting the child's body off the ground so the child is "walking" on his or her hands. The child should try to keep the back and legs straight. This may take some gentle practice for the child to master, but it is excellent for developing gross and fine motor skills. When doing this activity as a relay race, remember that it is for fun and not truly a race. Nevertheless, having that little bit of "hurry-up" pressure that excitement and competition can bring may really accelerate the development of important building blocks.

ABOUT THE AUTHOR

My enthusiasm for understanding the special needs population began while a student at the University of British Columbia in the School of Rehabilitation Medicine. The journey began when I was awarded seed money by the government of British Columbia to better understand the challenges of the disabled person during the International Year of the Disabled Person in 1981. Since moving to California in 1986, I have guest lectured at over 100 public speaking engagements locally and across the country in order to share my theories and test my ideas in front of my colleagues. It was a kind of trial-by-fire approach to better understanding mainstream thinking of my physical therapy* and occupational therapy (OT)* colleagues.

With an increasing understanding of my craft and a better perspective of my colleagues' way of thinking, I then began the study of the self. In both physical therapy and occupational therapy the main tool we use to help others is ourselves. Our own beliefs and experiences impact our ability to achieve a therapeutic rapport with our patient. To that end, I worked as an occupational therapist in the field of psychiatry to better understand the psychological makeup of my patients. I even studied history, comparative mythology and contemporary religion in hopes of determining what motivates each of us in our lives. My present field of interest is the science of neuroplasticity*. I am currently collaborating on a research paper to identify evidence of neuroplasticity in individuals with autism spectrum disorder* and in musical savants.

These diverse fields of interest continue to be the motivation behind my study of children and adults with disabilities. The first draft of this book was written in 2009, at that time, with ten years of data I had compiled. Suffering from profound insecurity about my writing skills, it wasn't until 2013 that I met my confidence-builder and writing coach, Julie Marsh. What happened next was a proliferation of writing. Julie told me, "Just write and write some more."

Soon categories of my patients' symptoms and their challenges became evident. Similarities in student and patient reports I had written were stacked in specific piles that were spread out on the floor of my office. These piles of reports became the chapters in this book. A clear pattern became evident that tied together these patients and students with their unique way of learning. I discovered that a unifying theory of looking at these challenges was possible.

Discovering this pattern turned on a light of understanding and provided clarity regarding the cause of this population's problems with learning in school, at work, and at home. I now believe that the answer to most learning difficulties lies in the vestibular, proprioceptive and tactile sensory systems. These systems are crucial to the brain's capacity to perceive, remember and motor plan.

In these pages, I provided strategies to promote healthy sensory processing* through the vestibular, proprioceptive and tactile systems*. You don't have to have a learning disability to profit from these ideas. Many of these strategies have been used in the field of sports medicine where a massive amount of scientific research has been focused on creating methods to enhance the ability of the brain and body to work cooperatively together. This research has illuminated how to promote the most ideal and high level human performance in the arena of athletics and, in addition, the best way to teach these high level athletic concepts to promote performance.

When I graduated from my occupational therapy and physical therapy (PT)* school, I worked with the Australian women's pre-Olympic swim team when they trained in my home town. Many of the activities we used to speed up their strokes were identical to those used by occupational therapists in schools to promote student performance. At the pool, the sport psychologist measured the athletes' swim times with and without the VPT* sensory facilitation* activities. Swim times were far faster following balance (vestibular-V), movement (proprioceptive-P) and touching/pressure (tactile-T) exercises. So it goes to show that VPT stimulation has a strong potential to raise the level of human performance, and promoting performance in the unique learner is what this book is all about.

The research into athletic performance is very useful for occupational and physical therapists because, by using these techniques, we can improve how the unique learner's body performs. We can help their ability to function in traditional social, classroom, sports and work settings. The unique learner can teach themselves strategies and techniques for later in life when they function more independently. The goal of this book, however, is not for your child to function "normally." Rather, the goal of *Unique Learner Solutions* is for your child to function "optimally" in order to develop into all that they can become.